BASIC
STATISTICS

Reports in the Police Foundation series are published as an information service. The analysis, arguments, conclusions and recommendations in this report are those of the author and not necessarily those of the Foundation.

British Library Cataloguing in Publication Data

Hibberd, Malcolm
    Basic statistics: a manual for police officers.
    1. Statistics. Information sources
    I. Title
    001.422

    ISBN 0-947692-16-9

Published by the Police Foundation
314/316 Vauxhall Bridge Road, London SW1V 1AA
Printed by Anthony Rowe Limited, Chippenham, Wiltshire.

CONTENTS

LIST OF FIGURES

LIST OF TABLES

FOREWORD

The pressures for results-based assessment and planning in the police service - in current shorthand, demonstrating value for money - have probably never been greater. While Circular 114/83 provides the most explicit statement of the need for better evaluation as a precondition for the most effective management of resources, the importance of assessment and monitoring is a recurring theme in government policy statements on the police. These pressures have led to an upsurge in interest in and demand for research by the police service. An increasing amount of that research is now being carried out within police forces themselves.

Although police forces are being asked to do more research and monitoring, research knowledge and skills within the service are in short supply. This book and its companion volumes are designed to provide a comprehensive guide to planning and carrying out research in the police service, and to its role in police management. Unlike conventional methodological texts, the books are aimed specifically at a police audience; they address police managerial concerns and use examples drawn from police work to illustrate research methods and problems. We hope they will become essential reading for any police officer who is asked to collect and evaluate information, whether for a small-scale survey of local users of police services, or for a more complex study of the effects of changes in, say, the patterns of shift work on police morale and police effectiveness.

The manuals are already proving their worth. They are used as a basis for Malcolm Hibberd's regular contributions to the Greater Manchester Police course on research skills, and the Research and Planning Carousel at the Police Staff College.

The Foundation would like to thank the Home Office for a grant towards the cost of writing and producing these manuals. If our readers have any comments or suggestions on their content, we would be very pleased to hear from them.

Mollie Weatheritt
Assistant Director, The Police Foundation

PREFACE

The uninitiated often regard research as inherently untrustworthy, as something that can be used to prove anything at all. Such a reaction ranges from a healthy and wholly desirable scepticism, to outright denial that research has anything at all to offer. The latter position comes into sharpest focus when statistics are at issue: tables of means, standard deviations and percentages send many people into a deep depression, to which the only antidote is a hackneyed joke about lies and damned lies, or about drunken men and lamp posts.

Statistics undoubtedly have a bad name in many quarters. And all too often it is the statistics themselves that are seen as meretricious, and not the disreputable researchers who are their frequent consorts. But in truth, statistics are neutral; they can be used to inform and illuminate, and they can be used to mislead and confuse.

Statistics can hardly be avoided in police research, concerned as it is with measuring inputs and outputs, work and results, effectiveness and efficiency. If statistics (and, more generally, research) are to be trusted as a management tool in the police service, it is essential that they be used appropriately, and with full awareness of their inevitable limitations.

Enlightened use of statistics is one of the main responsibilities of the researcher. Personal integrity is important here, of course, but it also depends on knowledge and understanding. This manual attempts to provide the basis for that knowledge and understanding.

Aimed at the complete beginner (all that is assumed is the ability to use a pocket calculator), the main uses of statistics are described, with an emphasis on using statistics appropriately, and with full awareness of their limitations. The distinction is consistently drawn between what the statistics say (which is precise, but often limited) and what they are taken to mean (which is the result of human speculation, with all the weaknesses that entails). The reader is encouraged to be cautious in interpretation: the researcher should be the mouthpiece for the data, never the other way round.

Chapter One introduces some fundamental concepts, and discusses the various types of data that are available. This is essential reading, since using statistics appropriately depends on understanding the nature of the data.

Chapter Two describes the basic methods of summarising data so that figures can be appropriately and accurately described. Step-by-step guides are given for working out different types of statistical description. This is followed up in Chapter Three with detailed instructions for representing data in graphical or diagrammatic form.

Chapter Four moves onto a different level. The earlier chapters are concerned merely with describing and summarising data. Chapter Four introduces the idea of statistical inference, which allows the researcher to go rather deeper into the data, to explore patterns and relationships. The basic concepts behind the notion of statistical testing are explored, and the chapter ends with a simple guide to some of the statistical tests that can be used in different situations.

The reader who needs to use statistical tests should consult a more advanced textbook on statistics (preferably one that covers the use of statistics in business, psychology or sociology). While comprehensive coverage of statistical techniques is beyond the scope of this manual, the last two chapters are devoted to two particularly useful techniques: Chapter Five to chi squared and Chapter Six to correlation. The uses of these techniques are described, and detailed, step-by-step instructions are given, with worked examples on facing pages.

Malcolm Hibberd
London, 1990.

CHAPTER ONE

INTRODUCTION TO VARIABLES AND DATA

BASIC CONCEPTS

Most research involves *measurement*: looking at something in the world, assessing it in some way, and drawing conclusions. The measurement usually involves numbers, and drawing the conclusions involves statistical analysis.

To understand the process of measurement, you need to understand three basic concepts:

- entities,

- variables,

- data.

These concepts are explained below. The process of measurement, and the methods that can be used, are covered in detail in Chapter Four of Research and Evaluation: A Manual for Police Officers.

Entities

Entities are the things you measure, although to call them *things* is rather misleading, as they include people and places, as well as more abstract, concepts such as events or organisations.

Just about anything can be measured, but two things must be remembered. First, you must know exactly what entities you are interested in; this involves being able to define them properly, and knowing why you need to measure them.

Second, a group of entities that are measured must have something in common, a shared feature which reflects the reason you are measuring them. So, for example, a group of people being measured could have one of the following features in common.

1

- residents on a particular housing estate;

- victims of robbery in a police division during 1989;

- detective constables in a police force.

These examples show that your definitions of the entities must be specific, specifying time and place where appropriate.

Variables

The most important basic concept in statistics is the variable. If entities are what is measured, variables are what the entities are measured on. The newcomer to research and statistics must understand fully what the term means, and get used to seeing the world in terms of variables.

A variable is a concept which can be used to draw attention to a similarity or difference between two entities. Variables can be found everywhere in life, though most of them will not be of interest. In research you will be interested in a small number of key variables. In important part of the planning stage of research is deciding which variables you need to look at to answer a research question (see Research and Evaluation: A Manual for Police Officers, pages 45-51).

To illustrate this, take the example of fruit. An apple and an orange differ in some ways, and are similar in others, some of which are shown below:

Differences	*Similarities*
- texture	*- edibleness*
- colour	*- availability*
- structure	*- shape*
- juiciness	

These seven differences and similarities enable us to compare apples and oranges; in fact, they can be used to compare any two fruits: raspberries and bananas differ in shape, but are similar in edibleness. They are features of fruits, features which vary from fruit to fruit. They can therefore be called variable features or, more briefly, *variables*.

A variable can be defined as *any feature that makes one thing different from or similar to another*. Hence, variables allow us to say how similar or different things are.

To illustrate this definition with a different example, police officers can be compared on an almost infinite number of variables (although only a few will be relevant in any single research project). Below are four examples of variables on which any police officer can be measured.

> *Height:* *one officer may be 69" tall, another 73"; or they may both be 71".*

> *Length of Service: one officer may have been in the job for three years, another for 27 years; or they may both have been in for 8 years.*

> *Whether they are firearms trained: in this example an officer is either one thing or the other: two officers may differ, one being trained, the other not; or they may be the same, both trained, or both untrained.*

> *Rank: any two serving police officers can be compared in rank. One may be a Chief Superintendent, another may be an Inspector; or they may both be Sergeants.*

Some variables give you numbers as the measurement (height, for example, or length of service); others give you a label or category (as with *firearms trained* or *not firearms trained*). This is covered more fully below (pages 6-9).

Police officers and fruits are only two examples of things that can be compared using variables. In fact, variables can be used to compare just about anything, including places, events and organisations.

The only condition for making comparisons on variables is that you must compare like with like - it makes little sense to compare a PC with an apple, for example. This brings us back to the importance of defining carefully, and in a way that is appropriate to the aims of the research. More importantly, it means only comparing one police subdivision with other police subdivisions, and not with a police division, or a whole police force.

3

Further examples

Below are some examples of the sorts of entities that are likely to be measured in police research, and the sort of variables they could be measured on.

> *ENTITY: police subdivisions*
>
> *Possible variables:*
>
> - *number of serving officers;*
> - *number of recorded burglaries in 1989;*
> - *size of population covered;*
> - *whether it has a microcomputer.*
>
> *ENTITY: arrests*
>
> *Possible variables:*
>
> - *what the arrest was for;*
> - *whether it involved force;*
> - *when it was made;*
> - *outcome or result (for example charge, caution, successful prosecution).*

The number of entities that can be measured is almost infinite, and each one can be measured on an almost infinite number of different variables. The secret of measurement in research is:

> - to select and define appropriate entities, and
>
> - to select and define relevant variables.

The key word here is *select*: although the possibilities are almost infinite, in practice the number of variables should be kept to a minimum. Having too many variables is a very common mistake, and one which makes results very difficult to analyse.

For more detailed discussion, see Chapter Four of <u>Research and Evaluation: A Manual for Police Officers</u>.

Data

When entities are measured on one or more variables, you end up with information. In research, information is called *data*. (The word *data* is plural; its singular, which is seldom used, is *datum*.)

Each measurement of one entity on one variable yields a single *data point*. A collection of these data points is called a *data set*. If the data set is organised and ready for analysis, it is called a *database*.

It is the data that are subjected to statistical analysis. They are a summary of a selected portion of the real world. The process of measurement by which data are produced is summarised in Figure 1.1.

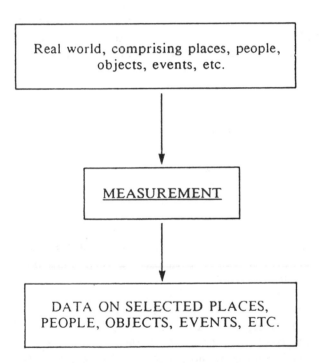

Figure 1.1 Summary of the process of measurement.

DATA AS NUMBERS

Data are usually recorded as numbers. There are two advantages to this: first, they take up less space that way; second, it makes them easier to analyse, especially if a computer is to be used.

Some data start off as numbers, such as the examples of height and length of service given on page 3. Data do not always start off as numbers, however. It is also explained on page 3 that the variable *firearms trained* gives you a description or category (an officer is either *firearms trained* or *not firearms trained*). The data can none the less be expressed as numbers, by a process of *coding*.

To illustrate this, imagine you are doing an analysis of recorded crime in an area, in which you take each recorded crime (the entity) and measure it according to the type of crime (the variable). In practice, this would entail going through the crime reports, simply recording the type of crime; you would end up with a series of descriptive labels, or categories. These can be turned into numbers by using *codes* - a different number applied to each category of crime, as in the following example:

CODE	TYPE OF CRIME
26	Robbery
27	Armed robbery
28	Theft
29	Shoplifting
30	Burglary

The codes here do not have any *numerical* meaning: 27 is in no way *greater than* 26 - they are merely numerical *labels*, an arbitrary and convenient way of recording data. Each number *stands for* the category. Data such as these, which begin life as a category and are then given numerical codes, are called *nominal*; nominal data are very important in police research, and are discussed at greater length on pages 7-9.

A worked example of how a series of measurements is transformed into numerical data is given in <u>Research and Evaluation: A Manual for Police Officers</u>, pages 144-147.

TYPES OF DATA - LEVELS OF MEASUREMENT

Data are derived from the real world by the process of measurement; they are a convenient record of the part of the world you are interested in for the purposes of your research. As such they represent an intermediate step in the research: they do not actually answer the research question, but they provide the means for doing so. Before the question can be answered, you must first establish what the data mean by analysing them.

This manual is largely concerned with how data are analysed. How this is done depends on what the data represent, and to analyse data appropriately, you must understand something about the properties of different sorts of data. Data vary according to their *level of measurement*. There are four levels, namely:

- nominal,

- ordinal,

- interval,

- ratio.

The last two types can be treated together; the differences between the resulting three types of data are discussed below.

Nominal data

This is the simplest form of measurement, and has already been introduced on page 6. Nominal data are derived by putting entities into appropriate categories. Each entity is given a label (normally numerical) indicating which category it belongs to. In essence, this involves *naming* the entities - which is why the data are called *nominal*; nominal data can also be described as *categorical*.

As explained above, although the categories are usually given numbers, the numbers do not have any *numerical* meaning - they are merely convenient (and arbitrary) labels, or *codes*.

For example, the entity *burglaries* can be measured on the variable *method of entry*, each burglary being classified as follows:

CODES CATEGORIES

1   Through an unsecured door
2   Through an unsecured window
3   Through a forced door
4   Through a forced window
5   Deception
6   Other
9   Not known

(Some researchers follow a convention of coding all *don't knows* as 9, or 99 if there are more than eight other categories.)

These categories clearly do not differ from each other numerically – the numbers are simply a convenient shorthand, reflecting different methods of entry. Each burglary will be given a code according to which category it falls into.

Although data such as these are not numerical in origin, they can none the less lead to numerical findings. If a sample of burglaries is classified in this way, you can count the number in each category, and produce a *frequency distribution*. For example, the following frequency distribution might be derived from classifying 200 burglaries:

FREQUENCY CATEGORIES

24   Through an unsecured door
21   Through an unsecured window
32   Through a forced door
78   Through a forced window
15   Deception
26   Other
4   Not known

Here the numbers tell you how many of each type were included in the sample. (The method for producing frequency distributions is described in Chapter Two.)

There   are   various   statistical   techniques   available   for

8

analysing nominal data, the most important being chi squared (see Chapter Five).

Other examples of nominal data include:

- a person's sex,

- type of recorded crime,

- whether an officer is firearms trained or not.

Data derived from questionnaire surveys are often nominal, the categories being the range of responses available for a particular question.

Ordinal data

Ordinal data are numerical, the numbers being assigned to entities on the basis of order, or ranking.

If three people run a race, a number can be assigned to each one according to who comes in first, second and third: the first person is assigned the number 1, the second 2, and the third 3. From this you know that the smaller the number, the better the position in the race: you know that number 2 was behind number 1 but in front of number 3.

Ordinal data carry limited information. In the race, the first three people get ranks 1, 2 and 3. However, this may not reflect their speed or times: there may have been a photo finish for first and second place, with the third person a long way behind; alternatively, the winner may have been a long way ahead of the others. It is impossible to say from the ordinal data.

Police ranks are another example of ordinal data. Police officers can be assigned numbers according to their rank, as follows:

1 = PC
2 = Sergeant
3 = Inspector
4 = Chief Inspector
5 = Superintendent
6 = Chief Superintendent

As with nominal data the numbers are used as codes, or labels; but in this case the numbers actually have a numerical meaning - the larger the number, the higher the rank.

This means that a wider variety of statistical techniques can be used in analysing the data. These techniques are summarised on page 61-63; a description of how to use them is beyond the scope of this manual, but can be found in other statistics textbooks. You also have the option of treating the data as nominal, and analysing them using frequency distributions and the chi squared test.

If data are to be treated as ordinal, you must be sure that increases in the numbers are consistent with increases in the underlying variable. Why this must be so becomes clear if you try to extend the rank classification system to include CID ranks. If you were to include separate categories (and code numbers) for CID ranks, you would no longer have ordinal data, because PC and DC, for example, are merely different - one is not a higher rank than the other.

Ordinal data can also be produced by simplifying a wider range of numbers. If you wanted to compare beat areas according to how much burglary they had last year, but only need a very rough guide to how many, you could use the following classification:

1 = 0-5 burglaries
2 = 6-20 burglaries
3 = 21-50 burglaries
4 = 51-100 burglaries
5 = 100+ burglaries

Once again the ordinal numbers (1 to 5) represent a consistent increase in the underlying variable, so that the higher the number, the greater number of burglaries happened on the beat: a beat scoring 3 will have had more burglaries last year than all the beats scoring 1 or 2, and less than those scoring 4 or 5. However, the distance between the ordinal numbers does not reflect a consistent difference in the *actual* numbers of burglaries: although 4 is twice 2, a beat with a score of 4 does not have twice as many burglaries as a beat with a score of 2 - look at the numbers to satisfy yourself that this is true.

Data from questionnaires are often ordinal. Any scales on which people are asked to rate their attitudes or experiences should be treated as ordinal. For example, if you want to find out how often people see a police officer on patrol in their neighbourhood, they can be asked to choose between the following categories:

1 = *Often*
2 = *Fairly often*
3 = *Sometimes*
4 = *Occasionally*
5 = *Rarely*
6 = *Never*

The choices are clearly in order, so that the larger the number, the less often the respondent reports seeing a police officer. But you can't say with any confidence whether the difference between *occasionally* and *rarely* is the same as the difference between *often* and *fairly often*. This is the limitation of ordinal data.

Finally, if you add a *don't know* category, its number cannot be included in the scale, as it bears no continuous relationship with the other categories.

Interval/ratio data

Interval and ratio data are the most sophisticated, and offer you the greatest flexibility in analysis. The difference between interval and ratio data is rather technical, and need not concern you too much; for the purposes of most police research, they can be treated as equivalent.

It is explained above that the positions of runners in a race (1 = 1st, 2 = 2nd, 3 = 3rd, and so on) are ordinal data: they carry limited information, telling us about the *order* of finishing, but nothing about *how far apart* they were.

Interval/ratio data do not have this limitation - they are numerical in the fullest sense of the word, referring directly to *quantities*. This means that the numbers tell you how much of something there is.

Let us say you are looking at the staffing of specialist squads in the force. One of the variables you might be interested in is length of service - how long members of squads have been in the job. This could be established by asking the officers, or by getting the information from personnel records. Each officer in the research would have a number indicating length of service, as with the following four:

OFFICER	LENGTH OF SERVICE
PC Smith	8 years
PC Harris	10 years
PC George	16 years
PC Jones	18 years

Note that these four officers have been placed in order, starting with the youngest in service - in other words, they are in ordinal positions. But the numbers mean more than that - *8 years* is a fixed and specified period of time, allowing us to say two things:

- *PC Harris has been in the job for longer than PC Smith, and by the same amount of time as PC Jones exceeds PC George in service - that is, two years. (This is what is meant by interval.)*

- *PC George has been in the job for twice as long as PC Smith. (This is what is meant by ratio.)*

The great advantage of interval/ratio data is that they can be analysed using means and standard deviations (see Chapter Two), as well as some more sophisticated and specialised statistical techniques summarised on page 62-63.

Other examples of interval/ratio data include:

- *divisional clear-up rates;*

- *number of recorded burglaries on a beats;*

- *time taken to respond to calls;*

- *the cost of different police operations;*

- *hours of overtime used by departments;*

- *intelligence (IQ) of police officers.*

Further examples

More examples of levels of measurement are shown in Figure 1.2.

VARIABLE (in italics)	LEVEL
A sample of residents classified by *ethnic group*.	NOMINAL
A sample of PCs ranked according to *length of service* (1 for the longest serving, 2 for the next, and so on).	ORDINAL
The *number of complaints* against two separate groups of officers.	INTERVAL/RATIO
IQ test scores of a sample of PCs and DCs.	INTERVAL/RATIO
A sample of PCs classified by *sex* and *relief* (two variables).	NOMINAL

Figure 1.2 Examples of variables and their level of measurement.

Summary

It is important to be able to identify the type of data you are dealing with, as this determines the type of statistical techniques that you can use.   The key features of the main types can be summarised as follows:

Nominal data represent *categories*;

Ordinal data represent *rank order*;

Interval/ratio data represent *quantities*.

13

CHAPTER TWO

DESCRIPTIVE STATISTICS

SUMMARISING DATA

Single measurements of single entities on single variables are rarely encountered in research: to know that one particular police officer has been in the job for 14 years, or that one particular recorded crime was a burglary, is of little use. What usually happens is that we measure a collection, or sample, of entities on one or more variables, and try to draw conclusions from the combined data.

Before conclusions can be drawn from a collection of measurements, the measurements themselves - the raw data - must be *summarised*, so that you are able to describe a whole sample, rather than separate individuals.

Summarising data is the most basic, and commonest, function of statistics; the methods for doing this are called *descriptive statistics*, and they are discussed in this chapter.

These methods can be divided into two types, depending on the *level of measurement* of the variable, as explained in the previous chapter. The first type of method, based on the frequency distribution, is for *nominal* and *ordinal* data, and is discussed on pages 14-24. The second type of method, involving combining numbers, is for *interval* and *ratio* data, and is discussed on pages 24-32.

SUMMARISING NOMINAL AND ORDINAL DATA

Since the numbers involved in nominal data are merely codes, having no numerical meanings, they can only be treated as representative of categories. Ordinal data do have numerical meaning, but since it is strictly limited (see pages 9-11) it is best to treat them in the same way. The method used is to count up the number of entities falling in each category, to produce *frequency distributions*.

Simple frequency distributions

A frequency distribution is simply a head count. It involves measuring all the entities (people, places, events, and so on) by placing them into the appropriate categories of the variable, and then counting how many have been put in each category.

The simplest example is the variable *sex*, which has two categories, *male* and *female*. A simple frequency distribution of 213 police officers from a subdivision might show that 172 were male and 41 female. This would be presented as follows:

MALE	FEMALE	TOTAL
172	41	213

This table could be described as a *breakdown* of the 213 officers by sex. This one variable is used to classify the sample, to give the frequency of occurrence of each category; because of this it is also called a *univariate frequency distribution* (that is, using one variable). The numbers 172 and 41 are called the absolute, or raw frequencies. Note that the frequencies for male and female add up to the total.

A simple, univariate frequency distribution can be produced for any variable, as long as each entity can fall into only one category. If there are a lot of categories (ten or more), then the frequency distribution becomes harder to understand, and so less effective as a summary of the data.

Percentage frequency distributions

Simple frequency distributions contain limited information. To make their meaning clearer and to make comparisons easier, they are usually presented as *percentage frequency distributions* as well. This presents the same information, but expressed in a different form.

Taking the same example of the 213 officers classified according to the variable sex, we note that 41 out of the 213 are female. This can be turned into a percentage by dividing the frequency (41) by the total (213) and multiplying the result by 100, as follows:

$$\frac{41}{213} \times 100 = 19.25\%$$

This shows that 19.25% of the sample are female. The percentage of male officers is worked out in the same way:

$$\frac{172}{213} \times 100 = 81.75\%$$

Note that if the two percentages are added together, the total is 100.00%. (The total of a set of percentages will sometimes be very slightly more or less than 100.00%; this happens when the decimals have to be rounded up.)

The percentages can then be added to the simple frequency distribution, to produce a table with both absolute and percentage frequencies, as shown below:

	MALE	FEMALE	TOTAL
Frequency	172	41	213
Percentage frequency	80.75	19.25	100.00

The totals for the percentage frequencies must be included.

In the next example, the variable is the type of drug involved in arrests for drug offences. Here there are more than two categories, and it is more convenient to list the categories down the page rather than across.

Type of drug	Frequency	Percentage frequency
Cannabis	655	76.61
Heroin	68	7.95
Amphetamine	81	9.47
Other	51	5.96
TOTAL	855	99.99

Note here that one of the categories is labelled *Other*. This is because in addition to the three main categories of drug, there are a number of different drugs which are not common enough to merit separate categories, but which taken together make up a reasonably sized category.

Frequency distributions for numerical variables

In the two previous examples the variables are sex and type of drug. The categories in these variables differ in type only: males differ from females; cannabis, heroin and amphetamines are different types of drug. In other words, the variables are *nominal*. Frequency distributions can also be produced for numerical variables.

Let us say that instead of classifying our 213 officers according to sex, we have classified them according to age, by placing each one in an age band (20-24, 25-29, 30-34, and so on) according to age last birthday (it is important to use a consistent definition of age).

The number of officers in each age band can then be presented as a frequency and percentage frequency distribution, as shown below:

Age band	Frequency	Percentage frequency
20-24	35	16.43
25-29	52	24.41
30-34	42	19.72
35-39	33	15.49
40-44	21	9.86
45-49	15	7.04
50-54	10	4.69
55-59	4	1.88
60-64	1	0.47
TOTAL	213	99.99

This table is a frequency and percentage frequency distribution of the officers by age. It is still a *univariate* frequency distribution, as there is only one *variable* (age), although it

17

happens to have more *categories* than the previous examples (nine). It is different from the previous examples because there is a numerical relationship between the categories.

Bivariate frequency distributions

The examples above are all of univariate frequency distributions - the breakdown of is by one variable at a time (sex, type of drug, age). While these provide an adequate summary description of data, they don't take us very far in interpreting data. To do that, we need to break down samples using two variables at once. The frequency distributions produced by doing this are called *bivariate frequency distributions*; other common names for them are *contingency tables* and *crosstabulations*.

In the first example (page 15), 213 officers were classified by sex; in the third example (page 17), the same 213 officers were classified by age. Each of these examples uses only one variable. The bivariate frequency distribution breaks down the same 213 officers by sex and age *at the same time*. The simplest way of doing this is to classify the males only by age; then do the same for the females; and finally to put the frequencies together. The resulting table might look like this:

Age band	Male	Female
20-24	27	8
25-29	38	14
30-34	34	8
35-39	27	6
40-44	18	3
45-49	13	2
50-54	10	0
55-59	4	0
60-64	1	0

The rows in the table represent the age categories, the columns represent the sex categories, and the frequencies are contained in *cells*. However, we also need *percentage frequencies*, and so some totals are needed. Two sets of totals can be produced, one for the rows (totalled by age category), the other for the columns (totalled by sex), as shown below:

18

Age band	Male	Female	TOTAL
20-24	27	8	<u>35</u>
25-29	38	14	<u>52</u>
30-34	34	8	<u>42</u>
35-39	27	6	<u>33</u>
40-44	18	3	<u>21</u>
45-49	13	2	<u>15</u>
50-54	10	0	<u>10</u>
55-59	4	0	<u>4</u>
60-64	1	0	<u>1</u>
TOTAL	<u>172</u>	<u>41</u>	<u>213</u>

The totals appear underlined in the *margins* of the tables; note that the two sets of marginal totals represent the univariate frequency distributions for the two variables taken separately: the row marginals give the frequency by age, and the column marginals give the frequency by sex.

Bivariate percentage frequency distributions

Now the totals have been entered, the percentages can be worked out. There are three ways of doing this - by row, by column, and by total.

Percentages by row

Each row of the table represents one age category, and contains the frequency of males and females of that age. The row percentages give the percentages of males and females *for each age group*.

The row percentages are produced by taking each row in turn, and calculating the percentages using only the figures in that row. So, in the first row, there are 27 males and 8 females, making 35 in all. Using the same rule as is given on page 16, we see that 27 out of 35 are male, so the percentage of males is

$$\frac{27}{35} \times 100 = 77.14\%$$

This means that of the officers aged 20-24, 77.14% are male. The same method can now be applied to females in that category:

$$\frac{8}{35} \times 100 = 22.86\%$$

This procedure is repeated for each of the nine age categories. The resulting row percentages are shown in Table 2.1 on page 22. The percentages in this table are added up to give 100% across the rows only.

The percentages by row (age) can be used to compare how many males and females there are in the different age groups.

Percentages by column

The second method treats the columns in exactly the same way. Each column represents one sex category, and contains the frequency of each age category for that sex. The column percentages give the percentages of the different age groups *for each sex*.

The column percentages are produced by taking each column in turn, and calculating the percentages using only the figures in that column. So, in the first column (males) there are 27 aged 20-24, 38 aged 25-29, 34 aged 30-34, and so on, making 172 in all. Thus, if 27 out of 172 are aged 20-24, the percentage of males of that age is:

$$\frac{27}{172} \times 100 = 15.70\%$$

This means that of the male officers, 15.70% are aged 20-24. The same can now be done for the next age group for the males:

$$\frac{38}{172} \times 100 = 22.09\%$$

This procedure is repeated for all nine age categories for the males, and then repeated for the females. The resulting column percentages are shown in Table 2.2 on page 23. The percentages in this table are added up to give 100% down the columns only.

The percentages by column (sex) can be used to compare the pattern of age between males and females. In this case, there appears to be a higher percentage of female officers in the younger age groups, showing that female officers are, on the whole, younger. However, to have confidence is this conclusion, you should carry out a test of statistical significance (in this case, chi squared, discussed in Chapter Five).

Percentages by total

The final method takes each frequency in turn, and works out the percentage using the total sample. The first frequency in the table, 27, represents the number of people in the male/20-24 combination. In other words, 27 out of 213 are males aged between 20 and 24, so the percentage is given by:

$$\frac{27}{213} \times 100 = 12.68\%$$

This means that 20-24 year old males make up 12.68% of the total sample. This is then repeated for the remaining 17 frequencies in the table.

This method gives each cell total as a percentage of the total sample. Since it does not treat the two variables separately, it is less useful and less likely to be used.

Which you use will depend on what sorts of questions you are trying to answer, and which comparisons are most appropriate. Any combination of these three methods may be used, although it is unwise to include all three sets of percentages, as the resulting table will be crowded with figures and difficult to understand.

If you want to compare age groups, then calculate percentages for each age; if you want to compare males with females, then calculate the percentages for each sex. The third method (percentage by totals) is probably the least useful, as it doesn't allow comparisons between sexes or age groups.

Univariate and bivariate frequency distributions can be presented visually, in the form of histograms and bar charts. For

Age band	Male	Female	TOTAL
20-24	27	8	35
	77.14	22.86	100.00
25-29	38	14	52
	73.08	26.92	100.00
30-34	34	8	42
	80.95	19.05	100.00
35-39	27	6	33
	81.82	18.18	100.00
40-44	18	3	21
	85.71	14.29	100.00
45-49	13	2	15
	86.67	13.33	100.00
50-54	10	0	10
	100.00	0.00	100.00
55-59	4	0	4
	100.00	0.00	100.00
60-64	1	0	1
	100.00	0.00	100.00
TOTAL	172	41	213

Table 2.1   Bivariate frequency distribution by age and sex, showing row percentages (by age).

Age band	Male	Female	TOTAL
20-24	27	8	<u>35</u>
	15.70	19.51	
25-29	38	14	<u>52</u>
	22.09	34.15	
30-34	34	8	<u>42</u>
	19.77	19.51	
35-39	27	6	<u>33</u>
	15.70	14.63	
40-44	18	3	<u>21</u>
	10.47	7.32	
45-49	13	2	<u>15</u>
	7.56	4.88	
50-54	10	0	<u>10</u>
	5.81	0.00	
55-59	4	0	<u>4</u>
	2.33	0.00	
60-64	1	0	<u>1</u>
	0.58	0.00	
TOTAL	<u>172</u>	<u>41</u>	<u>213</u>
	100.01	100.00	

Table 2.2 Bivariate frequency distribution by age and sex, showing column percentages (by sex).

a full description of these methods, using the same examples as are used in this chapter, see Chapter Three.

Bivariate frequency distributions can also be analysed to establish whether there is a relationship between the two variables. The technique used here is called chi squared, and is covered in Chapter Five.

SUMMARISING NUMERICAL DATA

In the example on pages 17-18, the variable age was treated as a series of categories. This was done by simplifying the original figures, with individuals being put into age bands, each of which spanned five years. While this is perfectly legitimate, it does not take full advantage of the precision of the data: the data could have been more fully exploited by taking their exact age last birthday.

If a variable is numerical then more sophisticated descriptive statistics are available to summarise data. There are two types - measures of location (or central tendency) and measures of dispersal.

MEASURES OF LOCATION

Measures of location summarise a group of numerical values, giving you an idea of what a typical value would be. To illustrate this, take following data, which are the ages (at last birthday) of 15 police officers:

26, 21, 35, 51, 24, 24, 22, 32, 26, 24, 28, 40, 24, 23, 29

While we have a measurement for each of 15 *individuals*, the sort of question that might be asked about a set of data such as this would be *how old is the sample of people?*

Just by looking at the figures you can get a rough idea of the answer to this question: most are in their twenties, with a couple of older people. But if we need a more precise summary, and one that is easier to communicate, we have a choice of three, namely:

- mode,

- median,

- mean.

Mode

The mode is the simplest method of summarising a set of numbers. To illustrate it, let us take the 15 ages and arrange them in ascending order:

21, 22, 23, 24, 24, 24, 24, 26, 26, 28, 29, 32, 35, 40, 51

The mode is simply the *most frequently occurring value*. With the exception of 24 and 26, each value occurs only once; 26 occurs twice, and 24 four times. The most frequently occurring value is therefore 24, so this is the mode.

The mode is for most purposes a very rough-and-ready guide, giving no indication that there are two values (40 and 51) that are considerably higher than the rest. There is also the problem that all the values might be different, in which case no mode can be given. Conversely, there may be two modes, when two different values occur equally often and more than all the other values. If the sample is large, then this is called a bimodal distribution (that is, one having two modes).

The mode is particularly unreliable if the sample is small.

Median

The median is simply the *middle value* when the data are arranged in ascending (or descending) order. It is the value which has the same number of values above and below it. Out of the 15 values of age given below, the middle one is the eighth largest (or, looking at it the other way round, the eighth smallest):

21, 22, 23, 24, 24, 24, 24, <u>26</u>, 26, 28, 29, 32, 35, 40, 51

In this example the median is 26. With an odd number of figures (as in this example), there is a single middle figure; there is no single figure where there is an even number of figures. Suppose that we had 12 instead of 15 measurements of age, as follows:

23, 25, 26, 26, 28, <u>29</u>, <u>32</u>, 35, 37, 37, 38, 41

Here, there are two middle values - 29 and 32. In this case the median is taken to be the value which is halfway between the middle two; for these data it would be 30.5. Notice that this value doesn't actually *exist* in the data set, but if it did, it would divide the sample into two halves, above and below itself.

The median is better than the mode, particularly for smaller samples, but it is still far from ideal. The main reason for this is that we are still unable to take the high scores into consideration, a weakness we noted with the mode.

Mean

The mean, or arithmetic mean, is the best way of summarising numerical data, providing the average score. Its chief advantage is that it takes the size of *all* the values into account. Working out the mean is slightly more involved, but still a simple procedure, involving two simple steps.

In calculating the mean, it is useful to know a little mathematical notation. Let us call the variable we have measured *x*. Since we have measured the age of 15 people, we have 15 different values of x. The number of values we have is called *n* (corresponding to the number of entities we have measured). The mean itself is called x, since it is the mean of variable x.

The formula for the mean of n values of variable x is:

$$\bar{x} = \frac{\Sigma x}{n}$$

The symbol Σ (Greek letter sigma) simply tells you to add up all the values of x. The mean is calculated by following the two simple steps directed by the formula.

STEP ONE Add up all the values of x.

$$\Sigma x = 21 + 22 + 23 + \ldots\ldots + 40 + 51 = 429$$

STEP TWO Divide the result by n.

$$\bar{x} = \frac{\Sigma x}{n} = \frac{429}{15} = 28.6$$

In summary, the three measures of location for our 15 age values give us the following results:

mean	28.6
median	26
mode	24

The mean is substantially larger than the mode and median because it takes into account the higher values at the upper end of the range. Because it does this, it is more representative of the sample as a whole, and therefore a better summary of the data.

MEASURES OF DISPERSAL

Measures of location tell you about how large a set of scores is as a whole, but it still doesn't tell us all we need to know about a set of data. To illustrate what it doesn't tell us, imagine taking the four reliefs at two subdivisions, A and B, and measuring the number of PCs attached to each.

The number of PCs on each relief at the two subdivisions is shown below:

SUBDIVISION A	SUBDIVISION B
Relief A - 36 PCs	Relief A - 28 PCs
Relief B - 32 PCs	Relief B - 47 PCs
Relief C - 29 PCs	Relief C - 21 PCs
Relief D - 31 PCs	Relief D - 32 PCs

If you work out the mean number of PCs on relief separately for the two subdivisions, you will find that they are exactly the same - at subdivision A there is a mean of 32 PCs per relief, and at subdivision B there is a mean of 32 PCs per relief. This suggests that the two subdivisions have the same relief strengths. In one sense this is true, but if you look closely at the data you will see that there is an important difference.

At subdivision A, the strength of each relief is fairly close to the mean value; at subdivision B, however, some of the reliefs have PC strengths which are very different from the mean - B has a lot more than average, C has many fewer. This is clearly an important piece of information: with such variations in strengths, subdivision B might give rather erratic coverage of the ground, while more consistent coverage would be achieved at subdivision A. In practical terms, some redistribution of strength might be called for at subdivision B.

Statistically speaking, the relief strengths are *dispersed* differently at the two subdivisions: at subdivision B they are widely dispersed, while at subdivision A they are grouped together more closely. The means tell us nothing about these differences, so what is needed is some measure of how widely dispersed a set of figures is. These are called *measures of dispersal*.

Two methods of measuring dispersal will be discussed here, the first rough-and-ready, the second more sophisticated. They are:

- range,

- standard deviation.

Range

The range is simply the difference between the highest and lowest scores. At subdivision A, relief A has the most PCs (36) while relief C has the fewest (29). The range is therefore:

$$36 - 29 = 7$$

At subdivision B, relief B has most PCs (47) and relief C the least (21). Here the range would be:

$$47 - 21 = 26$$

The larger the value of the range, the larger the spread of the scores. This is a very rough-and-ready guide to dispersal, which is useful because it can be worked out very quickly.

The range has a major limitation, however: it is exaggerated by *outliers* - values that are abnormally high or low. Say, for example, you have 100 observations, 99 of which lie between 45 and 67, the other value being 10. The range, being the difference between the highest and the lowest values, will be 67 - 10 = 57. However, the value 10 is clearly unusual - all the other values are much higher, and are closely grouped together. The range of 57 is exaggerated by what could well be a freak observation.

Using the range can, therefore, give undue weight to extreme values that are not representative of the data set as a whole.

Standard deviation

The best measure of dispersal is the standard deviation; the calculation uses the notation explained on pages 26-27. The formula for the standard deviation of n values of variable x is:

$$\text{s.d.} = \sqrt{\frac{\sum [x - \bar{x}]^2}{n}}$$

The calculation of the standard deviation is explained on pages 30-32, using the relief strength data for subdivision A presented on page 28. The standard deviation of the data from subdivision A, where the scores are close together, is 2.55; for subdivision B, where the scores are widely separated, it is 9.51, considerably larger. We see, therefore, that the greater the scores are dispersed, the larger the standard deviation will be.

For larger data sets this is a lengthy calculation. Fortunately, pocket calculators described as *scientific* will calculate standard deviations automatically.

Whenever you are summarising interval/ratio data, you should always give measures of location (preferably the mean) and dispersal (preferably the standard deviation).

Standard deviation - worked example

The data used in demonstrating the calculation of the standard deviation are the relief strengths from subdivision A, given on page 28. Newcomers to statistics are advised to repeat the steps using the data from subdivision B; the answer should be 9.51.

STEP ONE Calculate the arithmetic mean of the data set.

$$\frac{36+32+29+31}{4} = 32$$

STEP TWO For each separate value of x in the data set, calculate the difference between the value and the mean, by subtracting the mean from the value. Some will be negative, some will be positive, and some may be zero.

x	$\bar{x}$	$[x-\bar{x}]$
36	32	4
32	32	0
29	32	-3
31	32	-1

STEP THREE Take each difference score calculated in **STEP TWO** and *square* it - that is, multiply it by itself. Squaring the figures makes them all positive.

$[x-\bar{x}]$	$[x-\bar{x}]^2$
4	16
0	0
-3	9
-1	1

STEP FOUR Add up all the squared differences from **STEP THREE**.

$$16 + 0 + 9 + 1 = 26$$

STEP FIVE   Divide the total from **STEP FOUR** by n, the total number of values.

$$\frac{26}{4} = 6.50$$

STEP SIX   Take the square root of the result of **STEP FIVE**.

$$\sqrt{6.50} = 2.55$$

CHAPTER THREE

GRAPHICAL REPRESENTATION OF DATA

INTRODUCTION

Statistics are often easier to understand if they are presented as diagrams. There are five methods of presenting figures diagrammatically; each has its own uses, summarised in Figure 3.1.

METHOD	MAIN USES
PIE CHARTS	Used for showing the breakdown of a sample into its constituent parts.
BAR CHARTS	Used for the same purpose as pie charts, and also for bivariate frequency distributions.
HISTOGRAMS	Used for presenting frequency distributions, particularly where there are numerous categories of the variable; can be elaborated to show bivariate frequency distributions.
GRAPHS	Used for displaying the relationship between numerical variables, particularly where one is progressive, such as time.
SCATTERGRAMS	Used for displaying the relationship between two numerical variables.

Figure 3.1 Summary of methods of representing data diagrammatically.

Diagrams should be used only to *illustrate* numerical findings, not to replace them. They should be used cautiously, as they can be very persuasive, creating an impression of differences or trends, which may not be supported by statistical analysis. They can never be a substitute for statistical testing.

When and how to use each of these five methods is discussed in detail in the rest of this chapter.

PIE CHARTS

A pie chart is a circle divided into sectors, used to show how a sample of entities breaks down into different types. This means that it should be used on *nominal* data.

Pie charts illustrate frequencies and percentage frequencies. For example, the sample of 855 drug-related arrests discussed on page 16 is broken down by type of drug to give a frequency and percentage frequency distribution repeated below:

Type of drug	Frequency	Percentage frequency
Cannabis	655	76.61
Heroin	68	7.95
Amphetamine	81	9.47
Other	51	5.96
TOTAL	855	99.99

The total sample of 100% (near enough) is represented by the whole circle, or pie. The pie is then *cut* into proportionate slices or sectors, one for each of the four types of drug.

The pie chart is constructed as follows (see accompanying diagram).

A circle is made up of 360° (degrees); since the circle represents the whole sample - that is, the whole pie - 100% of the circle = 360°.

The first category, cannabis, accounts for 76.61% of the sample, and so should occupy the same percentage of the pie. We therefore need 76.61% of 360°, which is worked out as follows:

34

$$\frac{360}{100} \times 76.61 = 275.8° \text{ of the circle}$$

The same is then done for each of the other categories, giving us the size of the slice in degrees of the circle, as follows:

Cannabis	$\frac{360}{100} \times 76.61$	$= \underline{275.8°}$
Heroin	$\frac{360}{100} \times 7.95$	$= \underline{28.6°}$
Amphetamine	$\frac{360}{100} \times 9.47$	$= \underline{34.1°}$
Other	$\frac{360}{100} \times 5.96$	$= \underline{21.5°}$

Having calculated the size of the sectors, we are now able to construct the pie chart itself, as illustrated in Figure 3.2.

Pie charts are a very effective way of showing how a sample is divided up into different categories. The method only works if the whole sample can be classified in inclusive categories. This means that every entity must fall into one category, and one only.

Pie charts are not very useful if some of the categories have very small percentages: this makes the sectors small, difficult to label, and not very useful for the purpose of illustration.

How to construct a pie chart, step by step

STEP ONE Draw a circle with a pair of compasses; draw a vertical line up from the centre (that is, 12 o'clock).

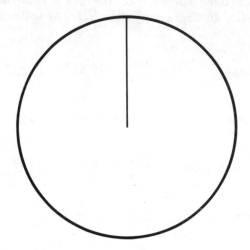

STEP TWO Using a protractor, measure the number of degrees of the first sector, starting from 12 o'clock. (For 275.8°, this will involve measuring 180° to 6 0'clock, then the remaining 95.8° from there.)

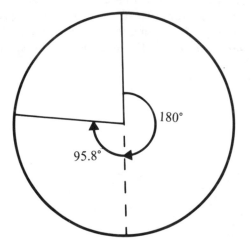

STEP THREE Starting from the line you have just drawn, measure the next sector (28.6°), mark a point and draw another line connecting it with the centre of the circle. This sector represents heroin.

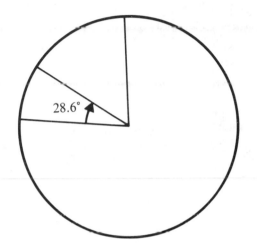

STEP FOUR Repeat this procedure for all the remaining categories. The last sector should take you back to 12 o'clock.

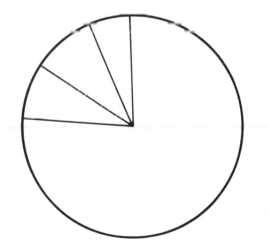

STEP FIVE To complete the job, each sector should be labelled, or shaded and a key provided. The pie chart should also be given an appropriate title. The result is shown in Figure 3.2.

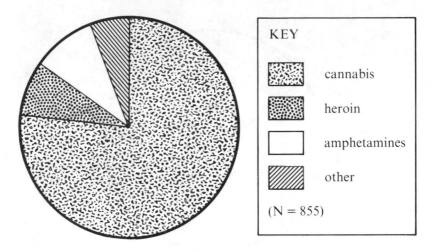

Figure 3.2 Pie chart showing breakdown of drug-related offences by type of drug (from frequency distribution shown on page 34).

BAR CHARTS

Bar charts use the same principle as pie charts, dividing up the area of a figure to illustrate the breakdown of a sample into its various categories. While a pie chart uses a circle, a bar chart represents the sample by a rectangle.

The whole rectangle represents the sample, that is 100%; it is divided up into sectors by measuring off the appropriate lengths, as shown in Figure 3.3, which presents the drug offence data used in the previous example.

Other

Amphetamine

Heroin

Cannabis

Figure 3.3   Bar chart showing breakdown of drug-related offences by type of drug (from frequency distribution shown on page 34).

For simple, univariate frequency distributions, either pie charts or bar charts can be used. Some people consider that pie charts give the most vivid impression, but they have the disadvantage of being fiddly to draw, involving compasses and a protractor.

Bar charts are particularly useful, however, for depicting bivariate frequency distributions (see pages 18-19). This is done by drawing separate bars for each category of one of the variables, and dividing up each bar according to the categories of the other variable.

If this method is used, the bar charts must be based on absolute frequencies and not percentage frequencies, as the bars may be of different sizes.

To illustrate this, take the example of an *activity analysis* looking at variations between the three shifts in the type of activity that patrol officers are engaged in. Such a study would seek to establish the mean time spent on each activity for each shift period. Table 3.1 presents the hypothetical results of such a study, showing the mean time in minutes spent on each of five pre-defined activities, separately for each shift.

Activity	EARLY TURN	LATE TURN	NIGHT DUTY
Uncommitted patrol	128	92	145
Dealing with incidents	31	53	62
Duties inside station	180	141	127
Refreshments	74	56	90
Other	67	138	56
Total	480	480	480

Table 3.1   Results of a hypothetical activity analysis, showing mean time in minutes spent on each type of activity, separately for each shift.

Presenting these data as a bar chart would involve drawing three separate bars, one for each shift; they would be of equal size because all shifts are 480 minutes long.

Each bar would then be divided up into five sectors according to the amount of time spent on each activity. This is made easier if the length of the bar can be related to the quantity being divided up. In this case, each shift period is 480 minutes. If the bar is made 96 millimetres high, each millimetre of the bar represents five minutes of shift time. For the early turn bar, the 128 minutes of uncommitted patrol can be represented by the top (or bottom) 26 millimetres (to the nearest 5 minutes). This is very slightly inaccurate, but will not distort the picture, especially as you should always present the figures as well as a diagram.

The resulting bar chart for this example is shown in Figure 3.4.

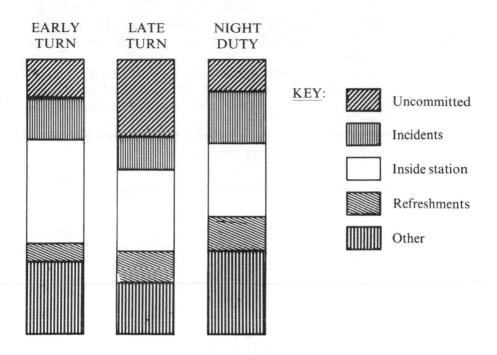

Figure 3.4 Bar chart for data shown in Table 3.1, showing time spent on each activity, separately for each shift.

HISTOGRAMS

A histogram is similar to a bar chart. It depicts a frequency distribution by means of a series of bars, the size of the bars being proportionate to the frequencies.

It can be used for all kinds of data, but if it is used for interval/ratio data, values must be put together into categories.

In its simplest form, the histogram is used for univariate frequency distributions. The bars sit on one of the axes (usually the horizontal) and extend up or out, according to the frequency. The bars can be separated from each other, or joined to make a continuous block.

A typical example is shown in Figure 3.5, using the age data from page 17. This is an illustration of how values are put into categories: age is an interval/ratio variable, which can take any value (although usually given to the nearest year); in this case, the data have been classified into a series of age bands, each spanning five years.

This histogram has nine bars, each one representing a different age group, and labelled in order along the horizontal axis. The height of the bars indicates the frequency of people in each age group, as shown on the scaled vertical axis.

When presenting histograms it is important to label both axes, and to give it a succinct and accurate title.

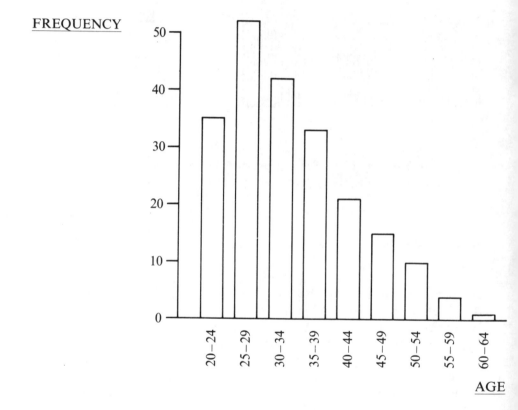

Figure 3.5 Simple histogram of age distribution using data from page 17.

Bivariate histograms

Like bar charts, histograms can be modified to depict more complex bivariate distributions. Figures 3.6 and 3.7 have been adapted from the previous example to include sex as well as age, using the data given on page 18. These are alternative ways of doing the same thing; which you choose depends on which appears to convey the best impression of the data.

In Figure 3.6, each bar is divided into two sections, one for each sex; the bars are shaded and coded to show which is which.

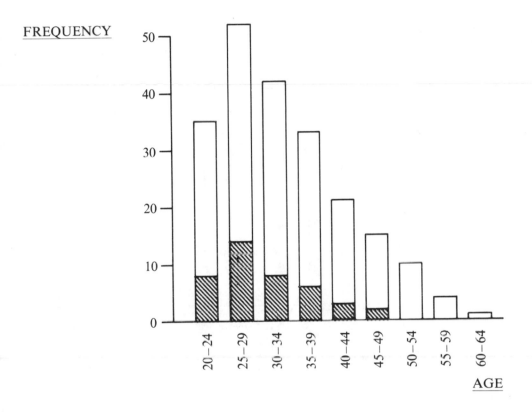

Figure 3.6 Bivariate frequency distribution of age, with bars broken down by sex (data from page 18).

In Figure 3.7, the same results are presented by using two separate bars within each age category, one for males, the other for females; again, the bars are coded for identification.

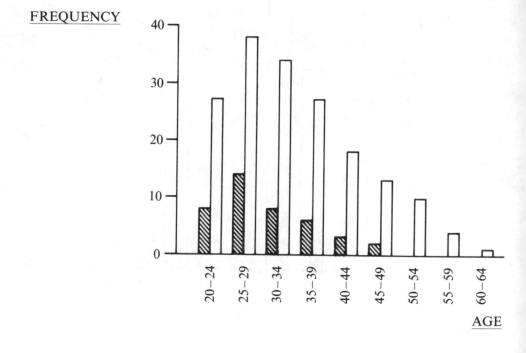

Figure 3.7 Bivariate frequency distribution of age with separate bars for males and females (data from page 18).

GRAPHS

A graph shows the relationship between two interval/ratio variables. It has two axes, one vertical (called the Y axis), the other horizontal (the X axis), each axis scaled to represent one of the variables. The variable on the X (horizontal) axis represents a continuous progression of some sort, usually time. This means that once the data points have been entered on the graph, they can be joined up to show a pattern of progression, or *trend*.

The points of the graph are plotted by taking pairs of measurements and entering them on the appropriate points on the graph.

Graphs are typically used to show changes over time. In the example used below, time is one of the two variables, and is shown on the horizontal axis.

The construction of a graph is illustrated using the hypothetical annual crime figures shown in Table 3.2.

YEAR	CRIMES RECORDED
1977	25,000
1978	17,900
1979	19,200
1980	39,600
1981	43,800
1982	22,900
1983	41,000
1984	34,700
1985	30,200
1986	45,600
1987	43,000

Table 3.2 Hypothetical annual crime data.

Looking at the figures alone, it is impossible to get much of an impression of the overall trend in recorded crime for the years 1977 to 1987; there are clearly some rather large fluctuations, but has crime risen or fallen overall? A graph gives a clearer picture, although it doesn't provide a definitive answer to the question.

45

The first thing to do is draw the axes, on appropriately squared paper. The X (horizontal) axis is to represent time, and should be marked out in equal intervals, representing the years 1977 to 1987. The Y (vertical) axis shows number of recorded crimes, and should be scaled appropriately. As the lowest number is 17,900 (1978), starting at 0 would waste space, so the vertical axis can start at, say, 15,000, with a broken line to show that the scale has been contracted here. The highest figure is 45,600, so the Y axis must go just beyond this point, and be marked out in equal intervals.

Once the axes have been drawn, the number of recorded crimes for each year is plotted. The points are then connected, starting with the 1977 point, joining that to the 1978 point, from there to 1979, and so on. The resulting graph is shown in Figure 3.8.

Looking at this graph, it does appear that there has been an upward trend in recorded crime from 1977 to 1987, but as there are very wide fluctuations between the figures, any conclusions from the graph alone would be very tentative. The conclusions would be strengthened if a *regression analysis* were carried out; this technique is beyond the scope of this book, but is described in more specialised statistics textbooks.

SCATTERGRAMS

Scattergrams are similar to graphs in using two axes, X and Y, to represent a relationship between two variables. In scattergrams, however, the points cannot be joined up, as they don't form a continuous progression.

With the example used to illustrate the graph on page 47, the intention was to show whether one variable (recorded crime) changed with the progression of another variable (time). Time can clearly only go in one direction; recorded crime can rise, fall or stay the same.

Scattergrams are used to show the relationship between two variables, where both can rise or fall freely. This means that there is no way of drawing a line to connect the points, as there is no *order* of points, as there is with time. Consequently, the points are left *scattered* on the two axes.

To illustrate the scattergram, the hypothetical data used are taken from Measuring Work and Performance: A Manual for Police Officers (pages 18-23), where the relationship between recorded

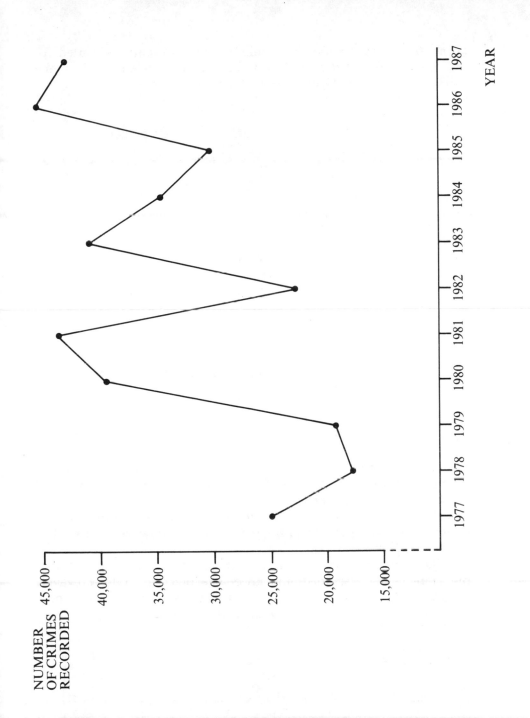

Figure 3.8 Graph of annual recorded crime figures from 1977 to 1987, using data from Table 3.2.

crime and detection rate is examined. Figures were presented for ten subdivisions, each measured on recorded crime figures and detection rate. The figures are repeated in Table 3.3.

Subdivision	Crimes Recorded	Detection Rate
A	8221	38.6
B	4527	50.1
C	8178	40.7
D	10731	36.6
E	3865	41.0
F	9255	37.9
G	6861	41.0
H	2590	46.6
I	6077	34.5
J	5267	38.7

Table 3.3   Recorded crime and detection rates for ten hypothetical subdivisions.

Drawing a scattergram is very similar to drawing a graph. Each variable goes on an axis, although, unlike graphs, it doesn't matter which goes on the X and which on the Y axis. In this example recorded crime will be put on the horizontal axis and detection rate on the vertical.

The axes are scaled and drawn, and the points plotted, in the same way as for graphs; the points, however, are left *unconnected*.

The resulting scattergram, shown in Figure 3.8, suggests that the more crimes recorded, the lower the detection rate; however, firm conclusions cannot be drawn from pictures, and this would need to be supported by a *correlation* analysis (see Chapter Six).

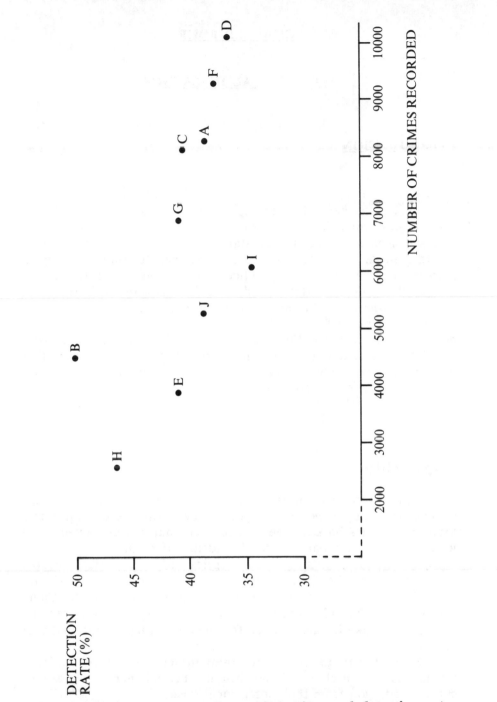

Figure 3.9 Scattergram of recorded crime and detection rate for ten subdivisions, using data from Table 3.3.

49

CHAPTER FOUR

STATISTICAL INFERENCE

INTRODUCTION

Descriptive statistics allow us to summarise data, but not to draw any conclusions beyond what the figures themselves say. If you need to go beyond the data, to draw more general conclusions, then you will need to use inferential statistics.

Inferential statistics allow the researcher to find meaningful patterns in the data. In practice, various tests and techniques are applied to the data, and calculations are performed to determine whether such patterns exist in the data.

Two particularly useful examples of these techniques are described in Chapters Five and Six of this manual, along with detailed instruction of how to carry them out. For other techniques, the reader should refer to one of the many more advanced statistics textbooks available.

Advice on the choice of technique in different situations is given on pages 61-63.

General advice

Although inferential statistics give you the facility to draw conclusions, they never allow you to be *certain* about anything: there will always be a degree of doubt in what you say, even when it is based on the apparently hard evidence of numbers.

None the less, don't be too sceptical about statistics. People often mistrust them, but statistics themselves are perfectly neutral - there is nothing inherently untrustworthy about them. The real problem with statistics is that they are often misused, by people who make inflated claims for their meaning, intentionally or otherwise.

The best way to avoid the unintentional misuse of statistics techniques is to understand the thinking behind them. (No advice can dissuade you from their intentional misuse.)

You should exercise caution when interpreting data. Figures can be very persuasive, particularly if they support what you want to say. If you understand how statistical inference works, you will be less likely to let yourself be persuaded by numbers, and consequently less likely to make unrealistic claims for your data.

Bear in mind that statistics are tools designed for use in well defined situations, and should not be used outside those situations. Always be aware of their limitations, especially when drawing conclusions.

GOING BEYOND THE DATA

The previous chapter explains how a set of data may be combined to give an easily understood description or summary. Once you have described a data set, you may well wish to go further, and use the figures to draw conclusions. This is the province of inferential statistics.

Drawing conclusions from data entails interpreting the figures, attaching some meaning to them. Attaching meaning to figures always involves going further than the figures themselves; it involves reading something into them.

Measuring change

As an illustration of this, take the very familiar example of recorded crime figures. Every police division or subdivision will compare recorded crime figures from one year to the next. The figures are easily available, and they seem to speak for themselves. In fact, figures never speak for themselves: they must be interpreted by people, and the interpretation is always a leap in the dark.

Suppose you are looking at subdivisional recorded burglary figures. Examining this year's figures, you find that there are fewer than there had been last year - in other words, they have declined, there has been a fall in the number of recorded burglaries. This line of reasoning is apparently innocuous, but let us analyse it more closely to see how it goes beyond the data.

We begin with the simple observation that there are fewer recorded burglaries this year than last. The next step is to say that the figures have declined, that this year's figure is lower than last year's. This is what the data tell you, and these first two statements are perfectly accurate.

The final step is to say that there has been a fall in the number of recorded burglaries on the subdivision. In a sense, this really says no more than the previous statement: there has been a change, the change has been in a downward direction, therefore there has been a fall.

The problem is one of implication: the fact that you *report* a change implies that it is *worth reporting*, that it means something. A fall in recorded burglary would seem to be a good thing, something worth celebrating. The problem lies in reaching this conclusion - that something good has happened, if you like - on the basis of a simple *numerical* change. It is this part of the statement that goes beyond the figures, and needs to be looked at more carefully. To do this, we need to examine the concept of natural fluctuation - or: *when is a change not a change?*.

Natural fluctuations

The problem with drawing conclusions from figures is that most figures that are used as data show a certain amount of natural fluctuation. These fluctuations show themselves as variations from month to month, from year to year, and from place to place; they may mean nothing at all.

Consider temperature as an illustration. In Britain, the average temperature in August is always higher than the average temperature in November. This difference *means* something, it being determined by the tilt of the earth as it orbits the sun.

We may also find that the average temperature in August 1990 is higher than it was in August 1989, perhaps by half a degree. This is unlikely to mean anything apart from the trivial fact that no two years are ever exactly the same. While the average temperature has clearly changed, the change carries no meaning - we could not attribute it to the greenhouse effect, for example.

The same problem applies to *any* data collected over time, including, for example, recorded burglary figures. Imagine that you have examined the burglary figures from two subdivisions, and found the following data:

> *in subdivision A, there were 542 burglaries in 1988, and 531 in 1989;*

> *in subdivision B, there were 612 burglaries in 1988, and 496 in 1989.*

52

Subtracting the 1988 figures from the 1989 figures, you can work out the change in recorded burglaries for each subdivision, as shown in the table below:

	Subdivision A	Subdivision B
1988	542	612
1989	531	496
Change	-11	-116
Percentage change	-2.03%	-18.95%

In both subdivisions there were fewer burglaries in 1989 than in 1988 - the numbers have fallen, as indicated by the minus sign on the change figures. But in subdivision B, the decline is much greater, regardless of whether you take the numbers (116, compared with 11) or the percentages (18.95%, compared with 2.03%).

The change at subdivision B may well mean something - it may reflect an *underlying* change in recorded burglary; at subdivision A, however, the change is so small that it probably means nothing. In conclusion, you would be more confident that burglary had fallen in subdivision B, than in subdivision A.

The simple reason is that all figures show some degree of fluctuation, from month to month, year to year, and place to place. While there may be a change in the *figures*, this may not actually mean anything about the underlying phenomenon (reported burglary in this case). This means that a slight rise is not really cause for concern, nor does a slight fall justify celebration.

The researcher is therefore faced with a problem: how big does a difference in the figures have to be before we can say that it means something? This is the central problem of statistical inference; it crops up *whenever or wherever* you are comparing figures, not just with changes over time.

To illustrate this, take another example of research that is concerned with differences between figures. Suppose you need to compare the work rates of the four reliefs at a subdivision, to see if there are any differences which need attention. One way of doing this would be to look at the arrest rate for each relief over the last seven week shift cycle, to see which relief has the highest and which the lowest rate (bearing in mind that arrest rate is only one of a number of possible *performance indicators* that could be used in this situation). Before drawing conclusions from any differences that you discover, you should think about the following question:

Over any seven week period, would you expect four reliefs to have *exactly* the same arrest rate?

The answer, of course, is no - there are bound to be minor fluctuations that may mean nothing at all. If one relief has made 189 arrests, and another has made 192, we would say their arrest rates are (more or less) the same. But there will be a point at which differences become so large that they must mean something, reflecting some underlying difference (such as in methods of working, supervision, or morale). If a third relief had made only 74 arrests in the same period, then there would appear to be something going on: the difference is so great that it could not be attributed to minor fluctuations.

The question is: *where* is the point at which the difference becomes too large to be explained in terms of fluctuations? Unfortunately, it is not possible to provide a final, definitive answer to this question. But the most satisfactory answer is provided by the procedures of statistical inference.

What is an inference?

An inference is a conclusion drawn on the basis of evidence. For example, if the sky is covered in low dark clouds, we infer that it is going to rain. We may of course be wrong: an inference is a sort of guess, with no guarantee of success. But it is more than a shot in the dark - it is an informed guess.

In statistics, inferences are made through the use of statistical tests; these are sometimes known as inferential statistics, as they are the statistics that allow us to make inferences. (This distinguishes them from descriptive statistics, which only allow us to describe data.)

To repeat, an inference is a sort of guess. But it is a guess in which we are *reasonably confident*. To indicate how confident we are in an inference, we use guidelines called *significance levels*.

The process of statistical inference is summarised in Figure 4.1, and outlined on pages 56-63.

STATISTICAL INFERENCE

is the process by which we distinguish

MEANINGFUL VARIATION

from

NATURAL FLUCTUATION

In doing this, we can never be entirely certain.

However, we can be

MORE OR LESS CONFIDENT

about our conclusions.

How confident we are about our conclusions

is indicated by

SIGNIFICANCE LEVELS

Figure 4.1 Summary of the process of statistical inference.

THE BASIC CONCEPTS OF STATISTICAL INFERENCE

The process of statistical inference is rather complicated, and depends on a number of concepts that will be new to most readers. The following section describes the basic concepts, using a straightforward example as an illustration; make sure you understand these concepts fully.

While the process is complicated, the aim of statistical inference is quite simple: it is to examine a pattern in a set of data - a difference, a change, or some relationship between variables - and decide whether or not the pattern is likely to be of genuine interest and in need of some further explanation.

Alternative interpretations

To begin with, let us take a research finding, expressed in simple, descriptive statistics:

> *in an average week, A relief make 48.6 arrests, while B relief make 53.2 arrests.*

It is perfectly clear that the two reliefs clearly have numerically different arrest rates, but there are two alternative interpretations of this:

> - *the difference is small, and could well be a random fluctuation, in which case there is no real, underlying difference between the two reliefs;*
>
> - *the difference is big enough to make us think there is a real, underlying difference between the two reliefs.*

Before the original finding can be interpreted, we have to choose between these two alternatives. We need to be able to decide whether a numerical finding is due to random fluctuation, or whether it means something more interesting.

We are helped in this by what statisticians know about how numbers behave: even random fluctuations show a certain amount of order. This enables us to work out how likely it is that a particular finding is due to random fluctuation. This depends on the concept of *probability*.

Probability

We all have an everyday understanding of probability, expressed in words and phrases such as *highly unlikely, possibly, very probably*, and so on. The same concept is used in mathematics and statistics, but here probability is measured rather more precisely, using numbers.

In mathematics and statistics, probability is a number that can take any value between one and zero; probability cannot be greater than one, nor can it be less than zero (that is, it cannot be negative).

If something has a probability of 1, then it is *certain* to occur. The sun is certain to rise tomorrow morning, therefore the probability of the sun rising tomorrow morning is 1. (Strictly speaking, no prediction about an event can ever be absolutely certain, but this is about as near to a certainty as you are ever likely to get.)

Probability values near to 1 (say 0.7 or 0.8) are high probabilities, and they mean that an event is *likely, but not certain*. A good bet, in other words. Burglar alarms provide a good example: most alarm calls are false alarms, therefore the probability of an alarm call being a false alarm is rather high (but not certain, of course, which is why they have to be taken seriously).

A probability of 0.5 is in the middle of the range, and means that an event is *just as likely to occur as not to occur*. Such a probability is often referred to as *evens*. When tossing a coin, it is just as likely to turn up heads as tails, so the probability of getting a head when you toss a coin is 0.5.

Probability values near to zero (say 0.1 or 0.2) are low probabilities, and they mean that an event is *unlikely to occur*; the closer to zero, the more unlikely it is. The probability of it snowing in London in October is low - it can happen, but it is unlikely.

Finally, a probability of 0 (zero) is an *impossibility*. If an object is dropped, it will fall downwards; it cannot fall upwards (at least, not under normal circumstances). Therefore, the probability of an object falling upwards is zero.

Probability and statistical inference

The concept of probability is central to statistical inference. To recap, the purpose of statistical inference is to establish whether or a finding means something, or whether it is simply due to random fluctuations.

As was explained on pages 56-57, statisticians and mathematicians know something about the behaviour of fluctuating numbers. This means that it is possible to take a given set of figures and work out the probability that they occurred by random fluctuation alone. This is done by carrying out appropriate statistical tests (see pages 61-63).

If there is a high probability of the findings occurring by random fluctuation alone, we cannot read anything into the finding; in that case, we would have to conclude that the finding is due to random fluctuation.

So, if we were to apply a statistical test to the arrest rates of the two reliefs, and find that there is a 0.6 probability of getting these results by random fluctuation, then we cannot report a meaningful difference in arrest rate between the reliefs.

By contrast, if there is a very low probability of the finding occurring by random fluctuation, then we can conclude that there is some other reason for the difference, and that the finding is meaningful.

So, with the same data, if our statistical technique were to tell us that there is only a 0.03 probability of getting this difference as a random fluctuation, this means the finding is unlikely to be due to random fluctuation alone. In other words, there must be some other, more interesting explanation.

In conclusion, then, statistical tests or techniques enable us to identify genuine findings, rather than findings that are due to random fluctuation; they do this by working out the probability of the findings being due to random fluctuation alone.

Choosing statistical tests or techniques

There is a variety of statistical tests techniques available for analysing data. Which one you choose depends on two main factors, the nature of the data, and what you are looking for in the analysis. A guide to choosing appropriate tests is given on pages 61-63.

It is important to select appropriate techniques for analysis, if you are to answer your research questions and draw valid conclusions. You should decide what sorts of test you are likely to use at the planning stage of research (see Chapter Two of Research and Evaluation: A Manual for Police Officers); this should enable you to collect your data in a form that can be properly analysed.

Statistical significance

In the previous examples, 0.6 was described as a high probability, and 0.03 was described as a low one. But how do we decide when a probability is small enough to indicate that we have a finding? In practice, statisticians use a series of arbitrary cutoff points called significance levels.

The first cutoff point is the 0.05 level. This means that if the finding has less than a 0.05 chance of occurring by random fluctuation, then we accept the finding as significant, and we say that it is statistically significant to the 0.05 level.

If a finding is found to be significant, it is unlikely to be due to random fluctuation alone; this means that the finding appears interesting enough to need explanation.

There are further significance levels of 0.01 and 0.001, as explained below. If a finding is significant to the 0.05 level, it may also be significant to the 0.01 or even the 0.001 level.

These cutoff points, or significance levels, are essentially arbitrary – there is nothing special about the number 0.05 that makes it preferable to 0.04 or 0.06; however, the significance levels of 0.05, 0.01 and 0.001 are a widely accepted convention.

The meaning of significance levels

Significance levels are simply probabilities. What they mean in practice is explained below.

0.05   If a finding is significant to the 0.05 level, it means that there is only a *one in twenty* chance of it being due to random fluctuation (1 divided by 20 = 0.05).

0.01   If a finding is significant to the 0.01 level, it means that there is only a *one in a hundred* chance of it being due to random fluctuation (1 divided by 100 – 0.01)

0.001   If a finding is significant to the 0.001 level, it means
that there is only a *one in a thousand* chance of it
being due to random fluctuation (1 divided by 1,000 =
0.001); in this case, we would say that the result is
highly significant.

(It is unfortunate and potentially confusing that the word
significant is used in this context, as it is a common word
outside statistics. For this reason, it is important in research
only to use the word in its precise, statistical context.)

The limitations of statistical significance

Statistical significance is only a *guide* to interpreting data.
There are three major limitations that must always be considered
when using inferential statistics.

1. Underlying. The first limitation is that significance levels
do not allow you to be *certain* of your conclusions - there is
always a chance that you have made a mistake in concluding that the
results are meaningful. In fact, the significance level also tells
you how likely it is that you have made a mistake. If the result
is significant to the 0.05 level, for example, this means that
there is a 1 in 20 chance that you are mistaken in saying the
finding is meaningful.

2. Explanation. The second limitation concerns *explaining* a
finding. If a finding turns out to be statistically significant,
that only tells you that there is something that needs explaining.
It says nothing about what the explanation is. For example, if you
find a significant difference between the arrest rates of two
reliefs, this only tells you that the finding is unlikely to be
random in nature. It is up to you to decide *why* the difference
arose. This will usually be done by collecting extra data. (This
illustrates the importance of planning your data collection
carefully, so that you collect the right data to enable you to
interpret your findings.)

3. Cheating. While statistics themselves cannot be dishonest, the
people who use them can be. One way to cheat is to increase the
number of statistical tests you carry out: the more you do, the

greater your chances of finding significance by chance alone. Computerised statistical packages make analysis very easy, and it is tempting to look at every possible relationship in a set of data, to find out which ones are significant. This approach, in which a data set is *trawled* for meaning, must be strictly avoided, as the conclusions would be invalid. You should only use statistical tests to answer the specific questions that the research is attempting to answer.

CHOOSING THE APPROPRIATE TEST

As has already been explained, thorough coverage of statistical techniques is beyond the scope of this manual. Anyone needing to carry out inferential statistical analysis should become fully acquainted with the concepts explained earlier in this manual, and then move on to a more advanced statistics textbook.

This last section of the chapter outlines the selection of appropriate methods of analysis. The test you use depends on two factors. First, the level of measurement of your data (see Chapter One) - that is, whether your data are nominal, ordinal or interval/ratio. Second, what you want to find out. Some of the things that can be done with data at each level are described below.

Tests for nominal data

The analysis that can be performed on nominal data is rather limited. It nearly always involves looking at the data to establish whether one variable is related to, or *associated* with another. In practice this means finding out whether the way an entity is classified on one variable has any bearing on the way the same entity is classified on another. This is often used in the analysis of questionnaire data, where the variables are commonly nominal.

The most popular technique for carrying out this sort of analysis is *chi squared*; it is discussed in detail in Chapter Five.

Other less common and more specialised techniques can be found in advanced statistical textbooks.

Tests for ordinal data

Ordinal data, which are based on rank order, also hold rather limited opportunities for analysis. Any data derived from attitude scales tend to be analysed in this way (see Chapter Five of Questionnaire and Interview Surveys: A Manual for Police Officers). Two types of analysis can be carried out - tests of correlation, and tests of differences.

Tests of correlation are likely to be used more often. They involve establishing whether two variables are related in such a way that as one goes up, the other goes up or down. (The concept as it applies to interval/ratio data is described in more detail in Chapter Six.) This could be used, for example, to establish whether people become more afraid of crime as they get older: fear of crime being an ordinal variable, usually measured on a four or five point scale. Among the techniques that can be used for this are *Spearman's rho* and *Kendall's tau* correlations. These and related methods can be found in more advanced textbooks.

Tests of difference are used where you have two groups of people, each measured on an ordinal variable, and you need to find out if the two groups have different scores, or ranks. The methods used - the most widespread being the *Mann-Whitney* test - involve comparing the ranks of the two groups. If you have three or more groups of people, more specialised techniques are available, under the heading *nonparametric analysis of variance*. Strictly speaking, tests of difference should only be carried out on randomly selected groups of people, and so are best restricted to experimental designs, such as those used in some evaluations (see Chapter Three of Research and Evaluation: A Manual for Police Officers).

Tests for interval/ratio data

The greatest range of analysis is available for interval/ratio data. As with ordinal data, analysis can be carried out to determine correlations and differences.

For correlations using interval/ratio data, the technique is known as the *Pearson Product Moment* correlation. This is covered in detail in Chapter Six.

Tests of difference include the *Student's t test* for two groups of people, and *analysis of variance (ANOVA)* for three or more groups. These can be found in most statistics textbooks. As with ordinal data, these tests depend on random allocation of people to the groups, and so should only be used in experimental designs.

In addition to these methods, interval/ratio data can be used to analyse trends, make predictions, and establish whether changes over time are significant or not. These methods depend on analysing the variability in a set of data (using the *standard deviation*, and related measures), and come under the heading of *regression analysis*. These methods can be found in most textbooks on statistics for business, economics or social science.

CHAPTER FIVE

THE CHI SQUARED TEST

INTRODUCTION

The chi squared test is one of the most widely used statistical tests in research on people. It is used to analyse the patterns in frequency distributions. It is particularly useful, since it can be applied to the simplest type of data - that is, *nominal* data (see pages 7-9); it can also be used on frequency distributions derived from *ordinal* data (see pages 9-11).

There are two applications of the chi squared test, one for univariate, the other for bivariate frequency distributions. The significance of chi squared is tested in the same way for both; to avoid repetition, this is described separately on pages 88-89.

Chi squared for univariate frequency distributions

This application is known as the *chi squared goodness of fit test*. It allows you to establish whether or not a simple frequency distribution conforms to a predicted pattern.

For example, suppose you know that of all the people who *apply* to become police officers, 63% are male and 37% female. If you then look at the numbers who are *accepted*, you can establish whether there is a sex bias in selection. If there were no selection bias operating, then you would expect those selected to be in the ratio of 63 males to 37 females. By comparing this expected pattern with the actual, observed pattern, you can answer the question of whether there is a selection bias.

How to carry out this test is described on pages 66-73.

Chi squared for bivariate frequency distributions

The second use of chi squared is for bivariate frequency distributions, also called contingency tables (see pages 18-19). Here, the test is used to establish whether the two variables are related to each other, or *associated*.

For example, if you have a sample of people measured on sex (male, female) and whether they smoke (smokers, nonsmokers), chi squared can be used to establish whether there is a relationship between sex and smoking. This is done by looking at the pattern of frequencies you have observed, and comparing it with the pattern you would have observed if there had been no relationship at all between sex and smoking.

This application is known as the *chi squared test of association*; its use is described step by step on pages 74-87. In the case of two-by-two contingency tables, the procedure is slightly modified, the variation occurring in Step Seven.

CHI SQUARED GOODNESS OF FIT TEST

The principle

The chi squared goodness of fit test is applied to simple, univariate frequency distributions, where a sample of entities has been classified according to one variable only (see page 15). The variable will usually be nominal, but the test can also be applied to frequency distributions derived from other variables.

The test works by comparing the actual pattern of frequencies (the *observed* frequencies) with a hypothetical pattern that you think they might conform to (the *expected* frequencies).

The sort of question that the test can be used to answer might be as follows. Let us say that you know that of all the people who apply to become police officers in your force, 63% are men and 37% women. If the selection of applicants has nothing to do with their sex, then you would expect the people who are accepted as police officers also to be (approximately) 63% men and 37% women. If the pattern deviates markedly from this, then this will be evidence that sex is an important factor in selection.

To test this, you would look at the numbers of males and females who are accepted, and compare this pattern with the number of males and females there *would have been* had they appeared in the same percentages as the applicants. Chi squared is then worked out. The value of chi squared tells you the extent to which the observed pattern deviates from the expected pattern.

Step by step guide for the chi squared goodness of fit test

How to work out chi squared in situations such as this is set out below, step by step. The instructions are set out on the left hand page, and the worked example follows these on the right hand page.

Where there are only two categories of the variable (as in this case: male and female), the procedure is slightly modified. The variation occurs in STEP FIVE.

STEP ONE

Set out the actual numbers of people (or other entities) in each category, as a simple frequency distribution. These frequencies are the *observed* frequencies.

STEP TWO

Decide on the pattern you want to compare the frequencies with - that is, that pattern you want to find out if the actual frequencies fit with or not. Express this pattern as percentages for each category of the variable.

STEP ONE

Out of a sample of 325 new recruits, 58 were women, and 267 were men. This gives us the following observed frequency distribution:

	OBSERVED
MALE	267
FEMALE	58
TOTAL	325

STEP TWO

Of the applicants, 63% were male and 37% were female. This is the standard against which the observed frequencies are going to be compared. If the pattern of applicants were reflected in the pattern of those accepted, then 63% of the 325 should be male, and 37% should be female.

STEP THREE

For each category of the variable, work out the frequencies you would expect to find if the pattern were the same.

This is done by multiplying the total sample size by the percentage for that category in the pattern, and dividing by 100. These are the *expected* frequencies, and they should be placed alongside or underneath the corresponding observed frequencies.

STEP FOUR

Taking each category in turn, subtract the expected frequency from the observed frequency (O - E). If the result is negative, remove the minus sign.

STEP THREE

Applying these percentages, 63% of 325 is 204.75, and 37% of 325 is 120.25. These are the expected frequencies for males and females respectively, and they can be entered in the table as follows:

	OBSERVED	EXPECTED
MALE	267	204.75
FEMALE	58	120.25
TOTAL	325	325

From this table it can already be seen that more males were observed than expected, and fewer females. Note also that the expected frequencies also add up to 325.

STEP FOUR

Subtracting the observed from the expected values for males and females, the following values are obtained:

	OBSERVED - EXPECTED
MALE	267 - 204.75 = 62.25
FEMALE	58 - 120.25 = (-)62.25

The minus sign on the second figure is ignored.

STEP FIVE (OPTIONAL)

Again taking each category in turn, subtract 0.5 from the result of Step Four, to give (O - E) - 0.5.

IMPORTANT! Step Five should only be carried out if there are only two categories in the variable. If there are three or more, Step Five is omitted.

STEP SIX

Take each result from STEP FIVE (or STEP FOUR if there are three or more categories), and square it - that is, multiply it by itself.

STEP SEVEN

Taking each category in turn, divide the result of STEP SIX by the *expected frequency* for that category.

STEP EIGHT

Add up all the results from STEP SEVEN. This is the value for chi squared.

STEP NINE

Work out the degrees of freedom (df) by subtracting one from the number of categories in the variable.

STEP FIVE

Since there are only two categories, 0.5 is subtracted from each figure, as follows:

MALE	62.25 - 0.5 = 61.75
FEMALE	62.25 - 0.5 = 61.75

STEP SIX

Squaring each value, we get:

MALE	$61.75^2 = 3813.0625$
FEMALE	$61.75^2 = 3813.0625$

STEP SEVEN

Dividing each value by the appropriate expected frequency, the following values are obtained:

MALE	3813.0625/204.75 = 18.623
FEMALE	3813.0625/31.709 = 31.709

STEP EIGHT

Adding these two values together, we get a value for chi squared:

$$= 18.623 + 31.709 = 50.332$$

STEP NINE

Since there are only two categories, there are (2 - 1) = 1 degree of freedom.

71

STEP TEN

The last thing to do is to establish whether the calculated value for chi squared is large enough to indicate statistical significance. Refer to pages 88-89 for instructions on how to do this.

STEP TEN

Referring to Table 5.1, our value of chi squared is higher than the critical values at all three significance levels. It can therefore be concluded that the observed pattern does not fit the expected pattern. Examination of the data show that males are more likely to be selected than females.

CHI SQUARED TEST OF ASSOCIATION

The principle

The chi squared test of association is used to test a relationship between two variables, where the data are in the form of a bivariate frequency distribution or contingency table. Each variable will have at least two categories, so the simplest contingency table would be a two by two; the test can be applied to contingency tables of any size, but it is very difficult to interpret large tables.

The principle for calculating chi squared involves comparing the actual pattern of frequencies (the *observed* frequencies) with the pattern we would have got had there been no association between the two variables (the *expected* frequencies). The difference between the two patterns is reflected in the value of chi squared: the larger the difference, the greater the chi squared, and the more evidence there is of an association.

Step by step guide for the chi squared test of association

Instructions for the calculation of chi squared are set out below, the instructions themselves appearing on the left hand page, with a worked example appears on the right.

The example is of study of stress in police work. Suppose you are doing this research, and that you want to find out whether there is a relationship between stress and shift work. You decide to select a random sample of 300 PCs from your force, and measure them on a range of variables, among which are the following:

Variable One: Shift work

To test the relationship between stress and shift work, you must measure shift work in some way. You decide to measure the amount of time officers spend on shift work in the course of a year, classifying them using three categories: those who, in the preceding year, have worked for <u>less than 1 month</u> on shift, those who have worked on shift for <u>between 1 and 6 months</u>, and those who have done <u>more than 6 months</u>. You therefore have three categories on this variable, which when applied to your sample of 300 *officers, gives the frequency distribution shown below.*

	≤1 month	1-6 months	>6 months	Total
Frequency	49	103	148	300

Variable Two: Sickness

Since a lot of sickness is thought to be related to stress, you decide to measure sickness (among other things), and classify the sample of officers according to whether they have had seven or more days off sick during the past year. This means that they either have had 7+ days off or they haven't - therefore there are two categories for this variable: 7 or more days off, and less than 7 days off. Classifying the officers gives the following frequency distribution shown below.

	7 or more days off	less than 7 days off	Total
Frequency	86	214	300

These two simple, univariate frequency distributions summarise the 300 PCs on each of the variables, but do not tell us what we need to know about the relationship *between* the variables. To find out about this we need to draw up a *bivariate frequency* distribution (see pages 18-19), and carry out a chi squared test. It is carried out in general on a *c-by-r* contingency table, where c is the number of columns and r is the number of rows.

STEP ONE

Decide which variable is to go in the columns, and which is to go in the rows - it doesn't matter which goes where. The number of categories in the column variable will be knowns as c, while the number of values in the row variable will be known as r.

STEP TWO

Draw up the contingency table, according to the number of entities in each combination of the c columns and r rows (there will be c x r combinations); these are the *observed frequencies*, and they are entered in the cells of the table.

STEP ONE

In this case, we shall have Variable One (shift work) as the columns, and Variable Two (sickness) as the rows.

Since there are three categories in the column variable, $c = 3$; and as there are two categories in the row variable, $r = 2$.

STEP TWO

In this example, let us suppose that the following frequencies were observed:

	<1 month	1-6 months	>6 months
7 or more days sick	7	19	60
less than 7 days sick	42	84	88

STEP THREE

Add up across the rows, and enter the totals at the end of the rows; then add up down the columns, and enter the totals at the bottom of the columns. These are the *marginal totals* (they are in fact the univariate frequency distributions of the two variables taken separately).

Finally, add up the row marginals to give the grand total (your sample size), and enter it in the bottom right hand corner of the table. The column marginals should add up to the same figure, so check that they do; if they don't, you have made a mistake in the addition.

STEP FOUR

The cells contain the *observed* frequencies. You must now calculate the frequencies that you would have got had there been no relationship between the two variables. These will be the *expected* frequencies.

To do this, take the first cell only (top left), multiply together the two marginal totals (one column marginal, one row marginal) to which that cell contributes, and divide the result by the grand total. This gives the expected cell frequency for that cell.

STEP THREE

Adding up across the first row, 7 + 19 + 60 = 86, which is entered at the end of that row; the second row adds up to 214, entered at the end of the second row. Adding up down the first column, 7 + 42 = 49, which is entered at the bottom of that column; the second and third columns add up to 103 and 148 respectively, which are entered at the bottom of those columns.

Adding up the column marginals, 49 + 103 + 148 = 300 (the sample size), which is entered bottom right; to check, the row marginals must add up to the same figure (86 + 214 = 300).

The revised contingency table is shown below:

	<1 month	1-6 months	>6 months	
7 or more days sick	7	19	60	86
less than 7 days sick	42	84	88	214
	49	103	148	300

STEP FOUR

The first cell (top left) belongs to the first row (marginal total = 86) and the first column (marginal total = 49).

Multiplying 86 by 49, we get 4214.

Dividing 4214 by the grand total, 300, we get 14.047 (to three decimal places), which is the expected frequency for the first cell.

STEP FIVE

Repeat the procedure for each cell, using the marginal totals for the row and column to which each cell belongs.

Draw up a new table, which has the observed and expected cell frequencies as columns one and two respectively.

STEP SIX

In order to proceed with chi squared, you must meet a condition called the 20% rule. This stipulates that chi squared *cannot* be used if more than 20% of the *expected* cell frequencies are less than five.

To check this, first establish if *any* of the expected cell frequencies are less than five - if there are none, you can proceed. If there are, you must work out what percentage of them are less than five. To do this, divide the number of cells with expected frequencies less than five by the total number of cells, and multiply the result by 100. If the result is 20 or less, you can proceed; if it is more than 20, the chi squared test will not be valid, and cannot be used.

If the 20% rule is not met, it is sometimes possible to get round it by collapsing two or more categories of one of the variables - that is, by treating two or more categories as one. This can only be done if there are good grounds for combining the categories.

STEP FIVE

The second cell (observed frequency 19) has marginal totals 86 (row) and 103 (column). Multiply these together to get 8858; divide this by 300 to get 29.527, which is the observed frequency for the second cell.

This is repeated for the remaining four cells. The observed (O) and expected (E) frequencies for each cell are shown in the new table, below:

Observed (O)	Expected (E)
7	14.047
19	29.527
60	42.427
42	34.953
84	73.473
88	105.573

STEP SIX

In this case, none of the expected cell frequencies is less than five, so we can proceed with the chi squared test.

STEP SEVEN

For the first cell, subtract the expected frequency (E) from the observed frequency (O), and enter the result in the third column in the new table. If the result is negative, remove the minus sign.

Repeat this for all the remaining cells.

IMPORTANT! If you are dealing with a two-by-two contingency table, then the procedure is slightly modified at this point. Once you have subtracted the expected from the observed frequency (and removed the minus if the result is negative), you must then subtract 0.5 from each result.

STEP EIGHT

For the first cell, square the result of Step Seven (O-E) - that is, multiply it by itself. Enter the result in the fourth column of the table.

Repeat this for all the remaining cells.

STEP SEVEN

For the first cell, subtracting E (14.047) from O (7), we get
-7.047; ignoring the minus sign, we get 7.047. Repeating this for
the remaining five cells, we get the results shown in the third
column of the table below:

Observed (O)	Expected (E)	O - E
7	14.047	7.047
19	29.527	10.527
60	42.427	17.573
42	34.953	7.047
84	73.473	10.527
88	105.573	17.573

STEP EIGHT

For the first cell, squaring 7.047, we get 49.660, to three decimal
places. Repeating this for the remaining five cells, we get the
results shown in the fourth column of the table below:

Observed (O)	Expected (E)	O - E	$(O - E)^2$
7	14.047	7.047	49.660
19	29.527	10.527	110.818
60	42.427	17.573	308.810
42	34.953	7.047	49.660
84	73.473	10.527	110.818
88	105.573	17.573	308.810

STEP NINE

For the first cell, divide the result of Step Eight - $(O - E)^2$ - by the expected frequency (E) for that cell. Enter the result in the fifth column of the table.

Repeat this for all the remaining cells.

STEP TEN

Add together all the results from Step Nine, that is, all the figures you have entered into the fifth column of the table.

The result is the value for chi squared for this contingency table.

STEP ELEVEN

Before interpreting chi squared, you need to work out a figure called *degrees of freedom* (df) for the particular contingency table you are working on, depending on how many rows and columns there are.

Degrees of freedom is calculated by multiplying the *number of columns minus one* by the *number of rows minus one*, the formula being:

$$df = (c - 1) \times (r - 1).$$

STEP NINE

For the first cell, dividing 49.660 by 14.047, we get 3.535, to three decimal places.

Repeating this for the remaining five cells, we get the results shown in the fifth column of the table below:

Observed (O)	Expected (E)	O - E	$(O - E)^2$	$\frac{(O - E)^2}{E}$
7	14.047	7.047	49.660	3.535
19	29.527	10.527	110.818	3.753
60	42.427	17.573	308.810	7.279
42	34.953	7.047	49.660	1.421
84	73.473	10.527	110.818	1.508
88	105.573	17.573	308.810	2.925

STEP TEN

Adding up all six values in the fifth column of the table, we get:

$$3.535 + 3.753 + 7.279 + 1.421 + 1.508 + 2.925 = \underline{20.421}$$

This is the value of chi squared for this table.

STEP ELEVEN

There are three columns, so c = 3, and two rows, so r = 2. Multiplying (c - 1) by (r - 1) we get:

$$(3 - 1) \times (2 - 1) = 2 \times 1 = \underline{2}$$

So this contingency table has 2 degrees of freedom.

STEP TWELVE

The next thing to do is to establish whether the calculated value for chi squared is large enough to indicate a statistically significant association. Refer to pages 88-89 for instructions on how to do this.

STEP THIRTEEN

If you have found that there is a significant association, the last thing to do is to attempt to explain it. Chi squared only tells you whether or not there is an association; it does not tell you exactly where it lies.

You can however, speculate by looking at the observed and expected cell frequencies. Cells with large differences between observed and expected frequency can help you locate where the association is, but remember that it is only speculation.

You should also remember that chi squared tells you nothing about the *cause* of any association.

STEP TWELVE

With df = 2, the critical values of chi squared (see Table 5.1 on page 90) for the different significance levels are 5.991 (0.05 level), 9.210 (0.01) and 13.815 (0.001).

Our value of chi squared (20.421) is clearly larger than all three, so we can conclude that there is a statistically significant association between shift work and sickness, at the 0.001 level.

STEP THIRTEEN

With a significant association, we can now attempt to describe the pattern.

Looking at the officers who have worked on shift for more than six months, more had been off sick for 7 days or more than would be expected if there had been no association (60, compared to the expected value of 42.427); similarly, fewer had not been off sick than would be expected (88, compared to 105.573).

Looking at those who had worked on shift for less than a month, fewer had been off for 7 days or more than would be expected if there were no association (7, compared with 14.027), while more had not been off sick for that long (42, compared to 35.953).

It would appear from this that the more an officer does shift work, the more likely the officer is to be off sick for seven days or more.

You cannot conclude from this that shift work is stressful, however. It could be that officers prone to sickness are more likely to be given light duties; also, shift work might lead to more injuries, and hence more sickness. Further information would have to be collected to help interpret such findings; this illustrates the importance of anticipating possible outcomes and collecting additional information accordingly (see Chapter Two of Research and Evaluation: A Manual for Police Officers).

TESTING CHI SQUARED FOR STATISTICAL SIGNIFICANCE

To test chi squared for significance, you need:

> - your value for chi squared,
>
> - the degrees of freedom for the contingency table,
>
> - the table of critical values for chi squared (Table 5.1 on page 90),
>
> - the instructions set out below.

STEP ONE

Look down the left hand column of Table 5.1 (labelled df) and locate the appropriate row according to your degrees of freedom; for example, if you have two degrees of freedom, then you will use the second row (df = 2).

STEP TWO

The value in the second column of the row (labelled 0.05) is the critical value at the 0.05 level; compare it with your chi squared value.

If your value is *smaller* than the critical value, then it is *not* statistically significant, and you need go no further.

If your value is *larger* than the critical value, then it is statistically significant to the 0.05 level. It may also be significant to the 0.01 level, so proceed to STEP THREE.

STEP THREE

The value in the third column of the row (labelled 0.01) is the critical value at the 0.01 level; compare it with your chi squared value.

If your value is *smaller* than the critical value, then it is *not* statistically significant to the 0.01 level, only to the 0.05 level, and you need go no further.

If your value is *larger* than the critical value, then it is statistically significant to the 0.01 level. It may also be significant to the 0.001 level, so proceed to STEP FOUR.

STEP FOUR

The value in the fourth column of the row (labelled 0.001) is the critical value at the 0.001 level; compare it with your chi squared value.

If your value is *smaller* than the critical value, then it is *not* statistically significant to the 0.001 level, only to the 0.01 level.

If your value is *larger* than the critical value, then it is statistically significant to the 0.001 level, which is as far as you can go.

df	0.05	0.01	0.001
1	3.841	6.635	10.827
2	5.991	9.210	13.815
3	7.815	11.341	16.268
4	9.488	13.277	18.465
5	11.070	15.086	20.517
6	12.592	16.812	22.457
7	14.067	18.475	24.322
8	15.507	20.090	26.125
9	16.919	21.666	27.877
10	18.307	23.209	29.588
11	19.675	24.725	31.264
12	21.026	26.217	32.909
13	22.362	27.688	34.528
14	23.685	29.141	36.123
15	24.996	30.578	37.697
16	26.296	32.000	39.252
17	27.587	33.409	40.790
18	28.869	34.805	42.312
19	30.144	36.191	43.820
20	31.410	37.566	45.315
21	32.671	38.932	46.797
22	33.924	40.289	48.268
23	35.172	41.638	49.728
24	36.415	42.980	51.179
25	37.652	44.314	52.620
26	38.885	45.642	54.052
27	40.113	46.963	55.476
28	41.337	48.278	56.893
29	42.557	49.588	58.302
30	43.773	50.892	59.703

Table 5.1 Critical values for chi squared.

CHAPTER SIX

CORRELATION

THE CONCEPT OF CORRELATION

Correlation is a widely used and important concept in statistics. It refers to the relationship between two variables, the extent to which changes one are consistently related to changes in the other.

Correlations are measured by a number called a *correlation coefficient*. This number has a maximum value of +1.0, and a minimum value of -1.0, and can take any value in between.

The meaning of a correlation coefficient depends on two factors, its *direction* and its *strength*. These are described below, and illustrated with examples on pages 92-93.

Correlations are most effectively illustrated by *scattergrams* (see pages 46, 49); examples for different types of correlation are given in Figures 6.1 to 6.3 on pages 94-96.

The direction of a correlation

A correlation can be positive, negative or zero; this indicates how the two variables are related to each other.

Positive correlation. A positive correlation is when two variables increase and decrease together - as one increases, so does the other. For example, if there is a positive correlation between the number of officers working at a division and the number of arrests made there, this means that *generally* (not invariably) the more officers working, the more arrests will be made.

Negative correlation. A negative correlation is where one variable increases as the other decreases, or *vice versa*. For example, a negative correlation between officers' length of service and the amount of traffic process they do, means (again, generally) that the *more* experienced officers do *less* traffic process.

Zero correlation. A zero correlation means that there is no relationship at all between the two variables, and that increases in one have no bearing on changes in the other. For example, a zero correlation between the number of complaints against an officer and the officer's height, means that an officer's height has no bearing whatsoever on how many complaints he or she has had.

The strength of a correlation

The strength of a correlation refers to how consistent the relationship is, regardless of its direction. The nearer a correlation coefficient is to 1 (either positive or negative) the more consistent will the relationship be - that is, there will be fewer exceptions to the general pattern.

The weakest correlation is zero, where there is no general pattern at all. The strongest correlation is +1.0 or -1.0; this is called a *perfect* correlation, and means that there are no exceptions at all to the pattern.

Perfect correlations are very rare. Evidence of a relationship is given by a strong correlation, say between 0.6 and 0.8 (or, if negative, between -0.6 and -0.8), though this depends on the size of the sample used to work out the correlation.

Correlation and causation

A correlation coefficient only tells you whether there appears to be a relationship between variables. It does not tell you that one variable *causes* the other. There *may* be a causal relationship, but a correlation coefficient cannot be used as evidence for its existence.

This illustrates the difference between statistics and their interpretation. You are free to speculate about the possible pattern of causality, but in your speculations you must do two things. First, you must show that you appreciate that there are alternative interpretations. Second, you must use evidence and reasoning to support the interpretation you choose. The statistics themselves are not enough to explain things.

Further examples of correlations

Perfect positive correlation. These are very rare, and examples tend to be rather artificial. A perfect positive correlation would be obtained if you measured:

- peoples' height in feet;

- the same peoples' height in metres.

Here you would be measuring the same thing, but using different scales. Someone who is 5'8" is taller than someone who is 5'7"; if their heights were measured in metres, this would still be true.

Positive correlation. A positive correlation that is not perfect would be obtained if you took all the subdivisions in a police force, and measured their:

- population;

- crime rate.

Generally speaking, the more people there are in an area, the more crime there will be. But there will, of course, be exceptions - heavily populated subdivisions with low crime rates, for example. But the general rule will hold on average across a large number of subdivisions.

Negative correlation. A negative correlation that is not perfect would be obtained if you looked at a subdivision over a period of time, and for a range of shift periods you measured:

- the number of arrests made by PCs;

- the proportion of the PCs available for patrol work.

The paperwork involved in making an arrest takes a PC off the street for some time. So the more arrests made, the less time will be spent on the street. But again, this will not always be the case - it is not a perfect correlation.

Compare the first example with the other two. In the first, the relationship is *always* true - there are no exceptions. In the other two examples, the relationship is true in most cases - there are exceptions, but the relationship holds *on average*.

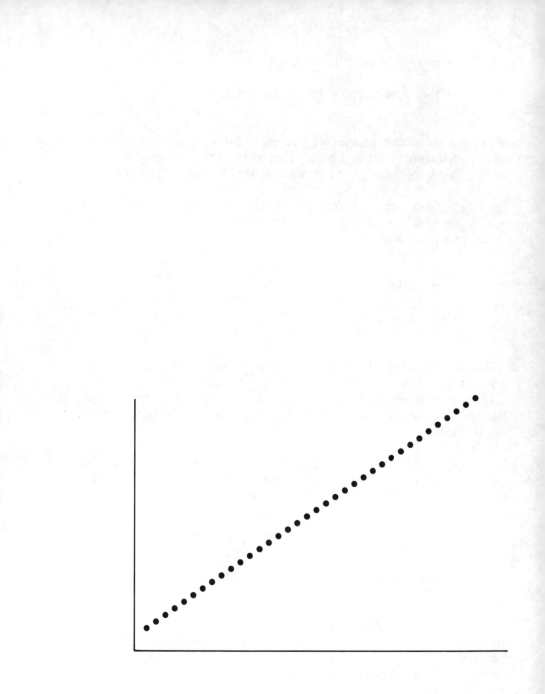

Figure 6.1 Scattergram of a perfect positive correlation.

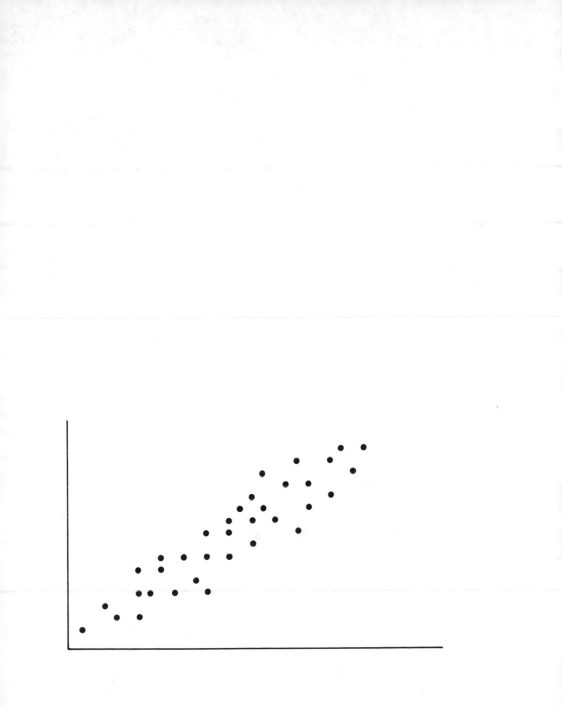

Figure 6.2 Scattergram of a positive correlation.

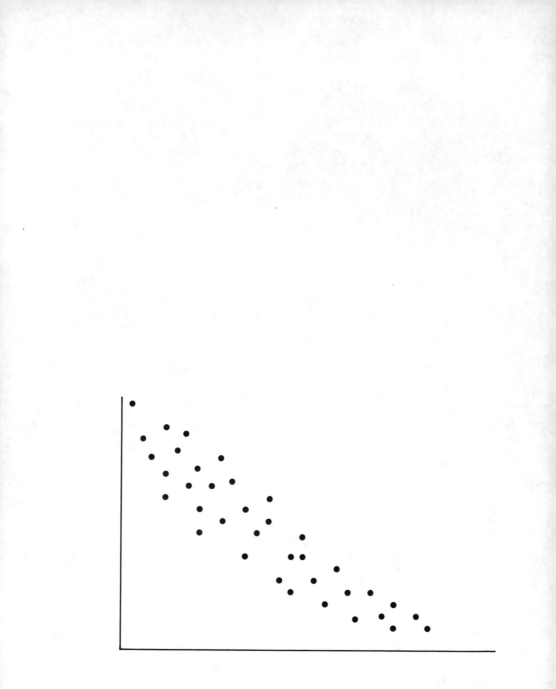

Figure 6.3 Scattergram of a negative correlation.

CALCULATING THE CORRELATION COEFFICIENT

The correlation technique described in the following pages is called the *Pearson Product Moment Correlation*. It can only be used on *interval/ratio* variables. If at least one of your variables is *ordinal*, then a different sort of correlation coefficient must be used. Some of these are referred to on page 62; they are described in most statistics textbooks.

A correlation coefficient measures the correlation between two variables at a time. We shall call these variables X and Y (it doesn't matter which is which). Each entity in the sample must be measured on both variables. In other words, each entity has a pair of measurements, one on variable X, the other on variable Y.

In the worked example, ten subdivisions are measured on recorded crime (variable X) and detection rate (variable Y) in 1989, giving the following data:

Subdivision	X	Y
A	8221	38.6
B	4527	50.1
C	8178	40.7
D	10731	36.6
E	3865	41.0
F	9255	37.9
G	6861	41.0
H	2590	46.6
I	6077	34.5
J	5267	38.7

The first thing to notice about these figures is that the values for X run to at least four figures. Calculating a correlation coefficient involves multiplying and squaring the numbers, so this means we will end up with some large and unwieldy figures. To avoid this, we can make the numbers smaller by dividing them by a constant factor, in this case 100. As long as all the X figures are treated in this way, this practice is acceptable. This is done in the example, and the resulting figures are shown in STEP ONE.

The method of calculation is set out below, with the step by step instructions on the left hand page, and the worked example on the right hand page.

STEP ONE

Decide which variable is to be variable X, and which to be Y. Which is which doesn't matter, but if you label the variables clearly from the start, there will be less chance of confusion.

Set out the figures for X and Y in a table, as shown in the accompanying example. Leave enough space for five columns; variable X should occupy the *first* column, and variable Y should occupy the *third*.

Decide if you need to scale down either or both of the variables; to do this, divide them by multiples of 10.

STEP TWO

a) Add up all the values of X (in the first column), and enter the sum at the bottom of the second column.

   The result of this step is called ΣX

b) Add up all the values of Y (in the third column), and enter the sum at the bottom of the second column.

   The result of this step is called Σy

   (The symbol Σ is called sigma, and means *sum of*.)

STEP ONE

The variable X is the number of crimes, variable Y is the detection rate. Since the values for X are large, they are all scaled down by a factor of 100. The resulting figures are set out in the following table:

Subdivision	X	Y
A	82.21	38.6
B	45.27	50.1
C	81.78	40.7
D	107.31	36.6
E	38.65	41.0
F	92.55	37.9
G	68.61	41.0
H	25.90	46.6
I	60.77	34.5
J	52.67	38.7

STEP TWO

a) Adding up all the values of X in the second column, we get 655.72; this number is entered at the bottom of this column.

b) Adding up all the values of Y in the second column, we get 405.7; this number is entered at the bottom of this column.

Subdivision	X	Y
A	82.21	38.6
B	45.27	50.1
C	81.78	40.7
D	107.31	36.6
E	38.65	41.0
F	92.55	37.9
G	68.61	41.0
H	25.90	46.6
I	60.77	34.5
J	52.67	38.7
	655.72	405.7

99

STEP THREE

For each entity in turn, take the value of variable X (the figures in the first column), square it (that is, multiply it by itself), and enter each result in the *second* column of the table. When this has been done for all entities, add up the results, and enter the sum at the bottom of the second column.

The result of this step is called ΣX^2

STEP THREE

Squaring the first value in the first column, we get 82.21 × 82.21 = 6758.48, to two decimal places. This is repeated for the remaining nine figures, and the results entered in the second column of the table.

Adding up all these values, we get 48915.85, which is entered at the bottom of the second column.

Subdivision	X	X^2	Y
A	82.21	6758.48	38.6
B	45.27	2049.37	50.1
C	81.78	6687.97	40.7
D	107.31	11515.44	36.6
E	38.65	1493.82	41.0
F	92.55	8565.50	37.9
G	68.61	4707.33	41.0
H	25.90	670.81	46.6
I	60.77	3692.99	34.5
J	52.67	2774.13	38.7
	655.72	48915.85	405.7

STEP FOUR

For each entity in turn, take the value of variable Y (the figures in the third column), square it, and enter each result in the *fourth* column of the table. When this has been done for all entities, add up the results, and enter the sum at the bottom of the fourth column.

The result of this step is called Σy^2

STEP FOUR

Squaring the first value in the third column, we get 38.6 × 38.6 = 1489.96, to two decimal places. This is repeated for the remaining nine figures, and the results entered in the second column of the table.

Adding up all these values, we get 16653.93, which is entered at the bottom of the fourth column.

Subdivision	X	X^2	Y	Y^2
A	82.21	6758.48	38.6	1489.96
B	45.27	2049.37	50.1	2510.01
C	81.78	6687.97	40.7	1656.49
D	107.31	11515.44	36.6	1339.56
E	38.65	1493.82	41.0	1681.00
F	92.55	8565.50	37.9	1436.41
G	68.61	4707.33	41.0	1681.00
H	25.90	670.81	46.6	2171.56
I	60.77	3692.99	34.5	1190.25
J	52.67	2774.13	38.7	1497.69
	655.72	48915.85	405.7	16653.93

STEP FIVE

For each entity in turn, take the value for variable X, multiply it by the value of variable Y, and enter the result in the fifth column of the table. When this has been done for all entities, add up the results, and enter the sum at the bottom of the fourth column.

The result of this step is called Σxy

We are now ready to calculate the correlation coefficient, r, according to the formula given below:

$$r = \frac{\Sigma xy - \dfrac{\Sigma x \, \Sigma y}{n}}{\sqrt{\left(\Sigma x^2 - \dfrac{(\Sigma x)^2}{n}\right)\left(\Sigma y^2 - \dfrac{(\Sigma y)^2}{n}\right)}}$$

STEP SIX

a) Multiply the result of STEP TWO (a), by the result of STEP TWO (b), then divide by the total number of entities, which we shall call N;

b) subtract this from the result of STEP FIVE.

STEP FIVE

Taking the first value of X (82.21), and multiplying it by the first value of Y (38.6), we get $82.21 \times 38.6 = 3173.31$, which is entered in the first row of the fifth column. This is then repeated for all the nine remaining pairs of X and Y values.

Adding up all these values, we get 25944.46, which is entered at the bottom of the fifth column.

Subdivision	X	X^2	Y	Y^2	XY
A	82.21	6758.48	38.6	1489.96	3173.31
B	45.27	2049.37	50.1	2510.01	2268.03
C	81.78	6687.97	40.7	1656.49	3328.45
D	107.31	11515.44	36.6	1339.56	3927.55
E	38.65	1493.82	41.0	1681.00	1584.65
F	92.55	8565.50	37.9	1436.41	3507.65
G	68.61	4707.33	41.0	1681.00	2813.01
H	25.90	670.81	46.6	2171.56	1206.94
I	60.77	3692.99	34.5	1190.25	2096.57
J	52.67	2774.13	38.7	1497.69	2038.33
	655.72	48915.85	405.7	16653.93	25944.46

STEP SIX

a) Multiplying the result of STEP TWO (a) by the result of STEP TWO (b), we get:

$$655.72 \times 405.7 = \underline{266025.60}$$

Dividing this by the number of entities (10), we get

$$266025 \div 10 = \underline{26602.56}$$

b) Subtracting this from the result of STEP FIVE, we get

$$25944.46 - 26602.56 = \underline{-658.1}$$

If the result is negative, it is vital that you don't forget the minus sign.

STEP SEVEN

a) Square the result of STEP TWO (a), and divide it by N (the total number of entities);

b) subtract this from the result of STEP THREE.

STEP EIGHT

a) Square the result of STEP TWO (b), and divide it by N (the total number of entities);

b) subtract this from the result of STEP FOUR.

STEP SEVEN

a) Squaring the result of STEP TWO (a), we get:

$$655.72 \times 655.72 = \underline{429968.72}$$

Dividing this by the number of entities (10), we get:

$$429968.72 \div 10 = \underline{42996.87}$$

b) Subtracting this from the result of STEP THREE, we get:

$$48915.85 - 42996.87 = \underline{5918.98}$$

(The result of this step cannot be negative. If you get a negative result, then you have made a mistake somewhere.)

STEP EIGHT

a) Squaring the result of STEP TWO (b), we get:

$$405.7 \times 405.7 = \underline{164592.49}$$

Dividing this by the number of entities (10), we get:

$$164592.49 \div 10 = \underline{16459.25}$$

b) Subtracting this from the result of STEP FOUR, we get:

$$16653.93 - 16459.25 = \underline{194.68}$$

(The result of this step cannot be negative. If you get a negative result, then you have made a mistake somewhere.)

STEP NINE

a) Multiply the result of STEP SEVEN by the result of STEP EIGHT;

b) take the square root of this.

STEP TEN

Divide the result of STEP SEVEN by the result of STEP TEN. This is the correlation coefficient, r. It must lie between +1 and -1 - if it doesn't, then a mistake has been made.

STEP NINE

a) Multiplying the result of STEP SEVEN by the result of STEP EIGHT, we get:

$$5918.98 \times 194.68 = \underline{1152307.03}$$

b) Taking the square root, we get:

$$\sqrt{1152307.03} = \underline{1073.46}$$

STEP TEN

Dividing the result of STEP SIX by the result of STEP NINE, we get:

$$-658.1 \div 1073.46 = \underline{-0.613}$$

This is the value for the correlation coefficient, r.

This resulting correlation is negative, so that as one variable goes up, the other tends to go down. The size of the coefficient indicates how strong that tendency is.

This correlation should then be tested for statistical significance, as explained in the final section.

Two observations can be made about this example. First, it is quite cumbersome on paper, but with a *scientific* calculator most of the work is cut out. However, when using a calculator, always keep a running note of the totals, and check calculations at least twice.

Second, the figures are very large, but the example is not unrealistic, since crime figures do go into thousands on an annual, subdivisional basis. Squared figures from these are even larger.

However, as explained on page 97, the figures can be scaled down. The easiest way is to take all the Xs (or all the Ys, whichever are the larger figures) and divide them all by 10, or 100, or 1000. As long as this is done to all the Xs (or Ys), the final result will not be affected.

TESTING THE SIGNIFICANCE OF THE CORRELATION

To test whether a correlation coefficient is statistically significant, you need to know the coefficient you have obtained, and the size of the sample used to calculate it.

Refer to Table 6.1 below, finding the row corresponding to your sample size (left hand column). If your exact sample size is not given, go for the nearest number *below* your sample size. Refer first to the column headed 0.05. If your correlation coefficient is larger than this, *regardless of direction*, then it is significant to the 0.05 level. If it is significant to the 0.05 level, refer to the next column to determine whether it is also significant to the 0.01 level.

	Significance levels	
Size of sample	0.05	0.01
5	0.755	0.875
10	0.576	0.714
15	0.483	0.605
20	0.425	0.538
25	0.380	0.488
30	0.338	0.440
35	0.320	0.417
40	0.300	0.394
45	0.280	0.370
50	0.262	0.346
60	0.248	0.328
70	0.233	0.308
80	0.220	0.290
90	0.206	0.272
100	0.194	0.255
150	0.158	0.209
200	0.137	0.182
250	0.125	0.163
500	0.088	0.115

Table 6.1 Critical values for the Pearson Product Moment Correlation Coefficient.